RETURN TO
STEVENAGE
CENTRAL
LIBRARY
SOUTHGATE
STEVENAGE
SG1 1HD
TEL 369441

G000081776

**Hertfordshire**
COUNTY COUNCIL
Libraries, Arts
& Information

G613.711

Please return this book
on or before the last
date shown or ask for
it to be renewed.

100% recycled paper.

-7 OCT 1996

28 OCT 1996

-5 JUL 1995          2 7 SEP 1995          6 MAR 1996

                    1 8 OCT 1995          9 APR 1996

2 8 JUL 1995                              1 3 MAY 1996

                     1 NOV                - 3 JUN 1996
                    - 8 DEC 1995

1 6 AUG 1995                              2 5 JUN 1996

                    - 5 JAN 1996          1 8 JUL 1996

-6 SEP 1995         - 7 FEB 1996          2 7 AUG 1995

L 33

# The Flexibility Factor

# The Flexibility Factor

## A Complete Guide to Flexibility in Sport

**Malcolm Brown and June Adamson**

**PELHAM BOOKS**

HERTFORDSHIRE
LIBRARY SERVICE

No
H30313 4772

Class
G 613. 711

Supplier | Price | Date
FARRIES | 14.99 | 8.5.95

PELHAM BOOKS

Published by the Penguin Group
27 Wrights Lane, London W8 5TZ
Viking Penguin Inc., 375 Hudson Street, New York, New York 10014, USA
Penguin Books Australia Ltd, Ringwood, Victoria, Australia
Penguin Books Canada Ltd, 10 Alcorn Avenue, Toronto, Ontario, Canada M4V 3B2
Penguin Books (NZ) Ltd, 182–190 Wairau Road, Auckland 10, New Zealand

Penguin Books Ltd, Registered Offices: Harmondsworth, Middlesex, England

First published in Great Britain 1995
Copyright © Malcolm Brown and June Adamson 1995
Line drawings copyright © Lesley Skeates-Bailey 1995
Photographs copyright © Dave Harrold 1995

All rights reserved.
Without limiting the rights under copyright
reserved above, no part of this publication may be
reproduced, stored in or introduced into a retrieval system,
or transmitted, in any form or by any means (electronic, mechanical.
photocopying, recording or otherwise) without the prior
written permission of both the copyright owner and
the above publisher of this book.

Typeset in Amasis by Selwood Systems, Midsomer Norton
Printed in England by Butler & Tanner Ltd, Frome, Somerset

A CIP catalogue record for this book is available from the British Library

ISBN 0 7207 2039 7

The moral right of the author has been asserted

# Contents

# Foreword

By Colin Jackson MBE

Stretching not only improves a person's flexibility but also plays a major part in reducing the risk of injury. As a hurdler, flexibility is an essential element of my training and I develop my flexibility through an extensive range of stretches. This range of flexibility allows my muscles and joints to move through their full ranges of motion.

If an athlete does not have the full range, then they cannot be getting the most out of their body. All-round flexibility will ensure that all your muscles work well and that you do not rely upon one specific group of muscles to their detriment while compensating for weaker ones.

People who attend one of my training sessions for the first time are always surprised at the amount of time I spend warming up. Although I always start a session with a two-lap jog, the remainder of the warm-up is dedicated to stretching exercises.

My stretching routine does not vary, which means that you will see me doing the same exercises in a cold climate as you will see me doing in a hot climate. A lot of the exercises I do are the same as any other athlete, with some specific to a hurdler. As I have already mentioned, flexibility is an essential key to technique over the hurdles and at 5' $11\frac{1}{2}$" I am one of the shortest hurdlers on the athletics circuit. As a result, I need to get over the hurdles as low as possible with my upper body flexible enough to bend over my lead leg.

The static exercises in the warm-up are combined with hurdles drills and PNF stretching (where a person applies force to a stretch). The PNF stretching is done with the help of a fellow athlete or coach before a race or after a training session during a massage.

Overall, I think that the importance of stretching cannot be over stressed and providing you receive guidance from someone who is knowledgeable about stretching or you take time to read this excellent book, you will not put yourself at risk by overstretching or doing the wrong type of stretch.

## About the Authors

**Malcolm Brown** is the Director of Sport and Recreation at the University of Ulster. He has studied Physical Education at the Universities of London and Leeds, gaining a B.A., B.Ed. and an M.A.

He is a National Event Coach for the British Athletic Federation with responsibility for women's distance running and has coached athletes who have competed at the Olympics, European Championships and the Commonwealth Games. The International Amateur Athletic Federation have employed him to tutor courses in Iceland, Egypt and the Czeck Republic.

In addition to coaching qualifications in athletics, Malcolm Brown has coached and taught football, swimming, volleyball and basketball. He has thirty years' experience as a competitive and recreational runner and competes in the occasional triathlon.

**June Adamson** received a B.Ed. (Hons) in Human Movement Studies from Dunfermline College of Physical Education, Edinburgh, in 1983 and an M.Ed. in Physical Education and Sports Science from the University of Glasgow in 1991.

She currently lectures in Physical Education at the University of Edinburgh, where she holds classes in step aerobics, popmobility, weight training, dance and other fitness-related activities. Over the past eight years she has devised and taught courses aimed at developing specific flexibility programmes for sports such as track and field, karate, netball, football, rugby, hockey and badminton. The participants include elite athletes, individuals recovering from sports injuries and people of all ages wishing to improve their flexibility. She also creates personalized flexibility programmes.

Outside the University, June is a consultant to, and assessor for Fitness Scotland, the governing body for fitness and exercise in Scotland. She is also a Judge in Modern Rhythmic Gymnastics and is a qualified Highland dancing teacher. June competed as a highland dancer for fourteen years and is currently a dancer and choreographer with Khoros Dance Theatre, a prominent Scottish amateur company.

# Acknowledgements

Many people contributed to the production of this book. We are particularly grateful to our excellent illustrator, Lesley Skeates-Bailey. The photographs were taken by Dave Harrold and reveal his insight into human movement. We are indebted to Susan Dumbreck, Kim Swanick, Louise Philip, Lindsay Thomson, Alan Chainey, Penny Clarke, May Cockburn, Alison Rose, Rona Brodie and the members of the 1993 Sports Bursars Group at the University of Edinburgh.

Finally, we would like to note that two people made this book possible, Judy and Ian. For your constant support and encouragement, we thank you.

# Introduction

Fitness is fun! Millions of people have discovered that when they are fit they cope more easily with the stresses of work, family and modern life. Consequently, jogging, aerobics, weight training and swimming are activities with participation rates substantially higher than two decades ago. Millions more have trained in order to complete a marathon, half marathon or ten kilometre race. These individuals have experienced the enormous satisfaction of rising to a major physical challenge.

Unfortunately, attempts to pursue fitness can be jeopardized by injury. Many injuries are the result of a lack of flexibility. Participation in sport or fitness activities tends to strengthen some muscles and leave others weak. Incorrect training methods will result in both the strong and the weak muscles becoming tight and inflexible. In our profession of physical education, we see individuals who have been given training advice based on an ignorance of the structure of the human body, on outmoded concepts and on superstition!

Flexibility is an aspect of training that is essential in many sports and activities. Yet it is often taught with little enthusiasm or completely ignored. The development of flexibility will prevent injury, reduce muscular tension, and help reduce stiffness. Appropriate flexibility for your particular sport will also contribute to the improvement of your techniques and thereby enhance your performance.

This book is written for a variety of people. Firstly it is for **sportsmen and women** who wish to make a major contribution to their fitness or sports performance through the development of a flexible body. *Flexibility for Sport* provides information on the latest and most effective stretching techniques. It is also a guide for **coaches** working in sports in which flexibility is not emphasized. Finally, **physiotherapists** working with sportspeople will find the menu of stretches a useful addition to their exercise prescriptions.

*Flexibility for Sport* is divided into five parts. The first part describes how the body moves, the basic function of the muscular and skeletal systems, and the factors that limit your potential range of motion. It addresses the important issue of which method of stretching is the most effective, and the authors state clearly their preferred methods. Part one concludes with a look at measuring flexibility and the important role of relaxation in developing flexibility.

The second part provides an insight into sports injuries. It describes the various causes of injuries and how to reduce the possibility of being injured. Advice is given on what to do and where to go for help if injury strikes. The information in this section is drawn from a unique analysis of data collected from the University of Edinburgh Sports Injury Clinic.

The third part of the book focuses on constructing a flexibility programme. It tells you the factors to take into account when you devise a programme for yourself or for others. We call upon our knowledge of the scientific literature, and many years of experience in advising sports participants of all standards, in order to devise these guidelines.

The fourth part is a practical guide to over 100 different stretches. Each stretch is illustrated and described in detail. The muscles that are particularly affected are described. The correct methods of stretching are identified.

The fifth part of the book provides fundamental stretching routines for twenty-three different sports and activities. The main characteristics of each sport are identified. We take these characteristics into account and create a warm-up schedule which can be used before training or competition.

It is vital that you perform the exercises as described in the text. Gentle, slow, careful stretching will produce substantial gains in flexibility. Poor quality stretching is a waste of time and can be dangerous. Follow the guidelines on page 26, and remember that every person is different. Some parts of your body will be tight, others less so. We present here a large selection of exercises from which you can construct your own individual flexibility programme. By incorporating flexibility training into your fitness programme, you will realize the potential that lies within your body.

| # The Theory of Flexibility

## Muscles, Movements and Joints

Improving your performance in sport requires an understanding of the way in which the body responds to exercise, rest and nutrition. Of prime importance is an understanding of the effects of exercise on the **muscular system**. Exercise can make muscles perform more efficiently or less efficiently, become stronger or weaker, become loose and fluent or tight and restrictive. To construct the most appropriate flexibility programme for your needs, you will need a basic understanding of how the body moves. This section will provide you with some of this information. More information is contained in the references listed at the end of this book.

The body moves by the complex interaction of the muscular, skeletal and nervous systems. The bones of the **skeleton** provide support and protection for your organs. They also provide the structure to which the muscles attach. The **nervous system** comprises the brain, spinal cord and nerves. It transmits and carries messages from the brain to muscles and organs. The muscles and skeleton, in conjunction with joints and the nervous system, make movement possible. A knowledge of the location and function of the main muscle groups and joints will help you understand movement.

**The Muscular System**

Muscles come in different shapes and sizes and have different functions. There are more than 450 different muscles in the body. Some are large, some small. They may be close to the surface and just under the skin, or deep inside the body. They may function to provide stability or to initiate movement. For example, the short deep muscles of the back provide stability for the vertebrae of the spine as we bend forward to lift heavy objects. The longer muscles on the front of the arm (biceps) contract through a much larger range and initiate bending at the elbow.

The muscles of the body can be considered in three categories, depending on their function: skeletal, smooth and cardiac muscle.

**Skeletal muscle** includes muscles in the legs, arms and back. They are active in movements that we consciously initiate. Because skeletal muscle is the only type of muscle under our conscious control, it is also

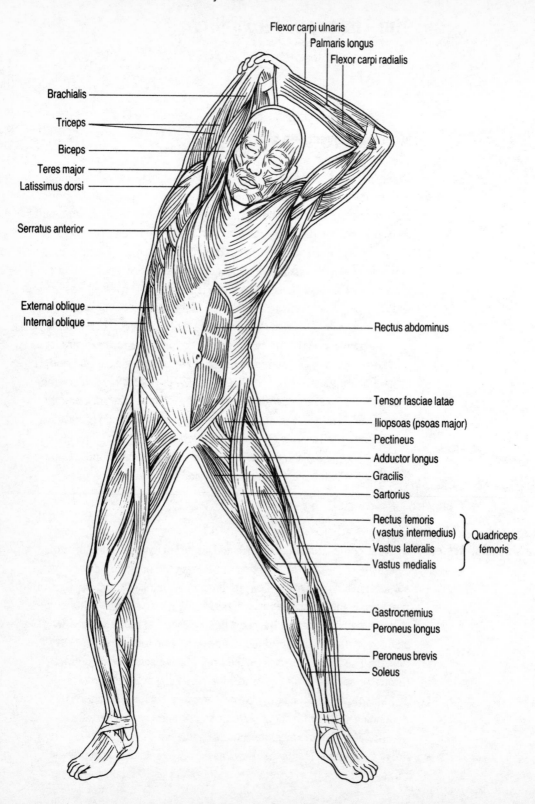

Flexor carpi ulnaris

Palmaris longus

Flexor carpi radialis

Brachialis

Triceps

Biceps

Teres major

Latissimus dorsi

Serratus anterior

External oblique

Internal oblique

Rectus abdominus

Tensor fasciae latae

Iliopsoas (psoas major)

Pectineus

Adductor longus

Gracilis

Sartorius

Rectus femoris
(vastus intermedius)

Vastus lateralis

Vastus medialis

Quadriceps
femoris

Gastrocnemius

Peroneus longus

Peroneus brevis

Soleus

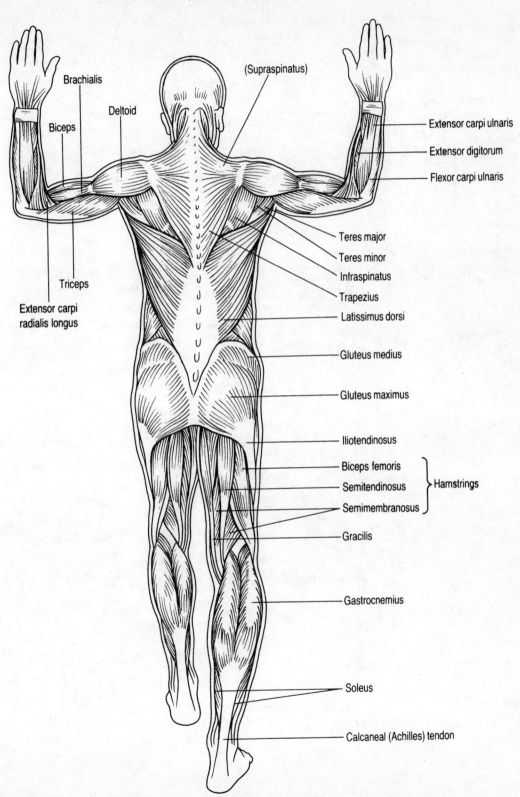

Brachialis

Biceps

Deltoid

(Supraspinatus)

Extensor carpi ulnaris

Extensor digitorum

Flexor carpi ulnaris

Triceps

Teres major

Teres minor

Infraspinatus

Trapezius

Extensor carpi
radialis longus

Latissimus dorsi

Gluteus medius

Gluteus maximus

Iliotendinosus

Biceps femoris

Semitendinosus  } Hamstrings

Semimembranosus

Gracilis

Gastrocnemius

Soleus

Calcaneal (Achilles) tendon

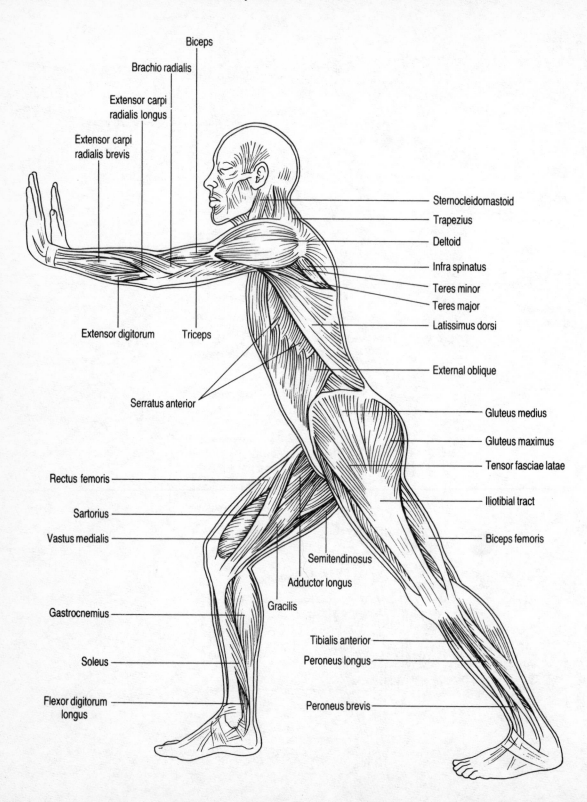

Biceps

Brachio radialis

Extensor carpi
radialis longus

Extensor carpi
radialis brevis

Extensor digitorum

Triceps

Serratus anterior

Sternocleidomastoid

Trapezius

Deltoid

Infra spinatus

Teres minor

Teres major

Latissimus dorsi

External oblique

Gluteus medius

Gluteus maximus

Tensor fasciae latae

Iliotibial tract

Biceps femoris

Rectus femoris

Sartorius

Vastus medialis

Semitendinosus

Adductor longus

Gracilis

Gastrocnemius

Soleus

Flexor digitorum
longus

Tibialis anterior

Peroneus longus

Peroneus brevis

called **voluntary muscle**. For example, if we wish to start to run, the brain will transmit electrical impulses along the central and peripheral nervous system to the relevant groups of skeletal muscle to initiate the appropriate movements. Skeletal muscle has a striped (striated) appearance.

**Smooth muscle** is found in the walls of organs such as the stomach, bladder and lungs. Unlike skeletal muscle, it is not striated and is not under voluntary control.

**Cardiac muscle** is dedicated to maintaining the function of the heart and is located in and near the heart. Cardiac muscle, like skeletal muscle, is striated, but it is not voluntary.

In this book, we are only concerned with skeletal muscle because it plays the main role in moving the body. The other categories of muscle, however, do play a part in assisting exercise, particularly in the transport of blood around the body to the skeletal muscle.

A muscle that contracts produces **tension** within the muscle. The muscle may shorten and appear to become larger and more bulky. When you hold a heavy book in one hand and lift it by bending your elbow, the biceps contract, develop tension and shorten. The biceps, when shortened, appears bulkier than in its resting state.

However, muscle can also develop tension when it **lengthens** and elongates. Imagine holding the same heavy book in one hand and lowering it slowly to a table by straightening (extending) the elbow. You will feel the tension in the muscle at the front of the arm. Muscle can develop tension both when it shortens and when it lengthens.

It is vital to realize that the term **contraction** refers to the electrochemical process of generating tension within a muscle. Muscles do not always shorten during contraction.

The development of flexibility through a training programme depends upon a muscle lengthening, stretching and relaxing. To understand the phenomena of tension, contraction, lengthening and stretching, it is necessary to understand the structure of muscle.

## Structure of Muscle

Skeletal muscle is made up of hundreds of muscle fibres. Each **fibre** consists of a series of layers, with each layer significantly different from each other. The fibre is made up of **filaments** of different sizes. The filaments lie in parallel lines and give skeletal muscle its striped appearance. When a muscle **contracts**, the smaller filaments (actin) and the larger filaments (myosin) slide together and interconnect. As a result, the muscle is shortened and it produces tension. The muscle **relaxes** by disconnecting the actin and myosin filaments, which enables them to slide apart. Through

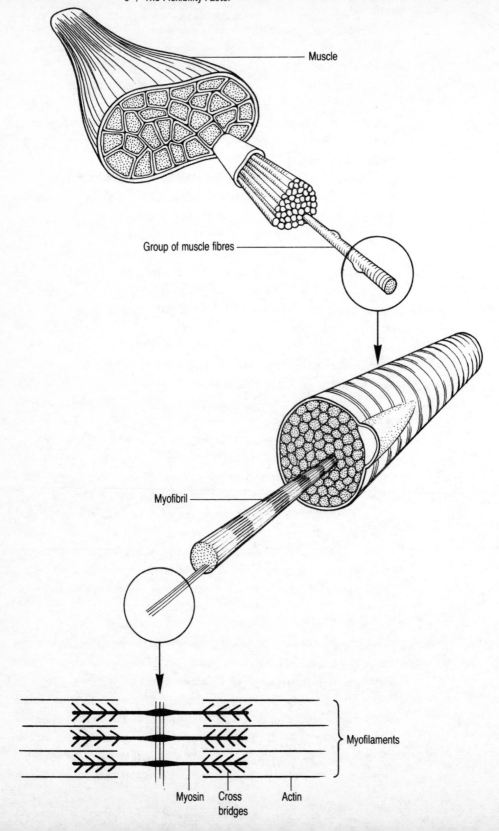

Muscle

Group of muscle fibres

Myofibril

Myofilaments

Myosin

Cross bridges

Actin

this process, the contracted muscle is restored to its original resting length.

In contrast, when muscle is stretched a reverse process occurs and the filaments reverse the interlinking effect. They become uncoupled.

**Muscular Movements**

When a muscle contracts and develops tension, it pulls on the bone and movement may take place. Muscle attaches to bones at two or more points. Skeletal muscle normally attaches to the bone by tendons. In any particular muscle, the attachment point that moves the least is called the **origin**, and the end of the muscle that moves the most is called the **insertion**.

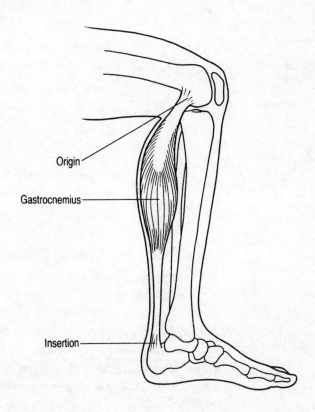

Movement will take place if the tension developed within the muscle is greater than the external forces it encounters. If the external forces encountered are greater than the muscle can generate, then no movement can occur.

In **dynamic muscular action** the origin and insertion of muscle are affected by changes in the muscle length. The origin and insertion of each muscle are either moving towards each other of away from each other. If the external force exerted on a muscle results in the opposite ends of the muscle being brought towards each other, then the muscle is working

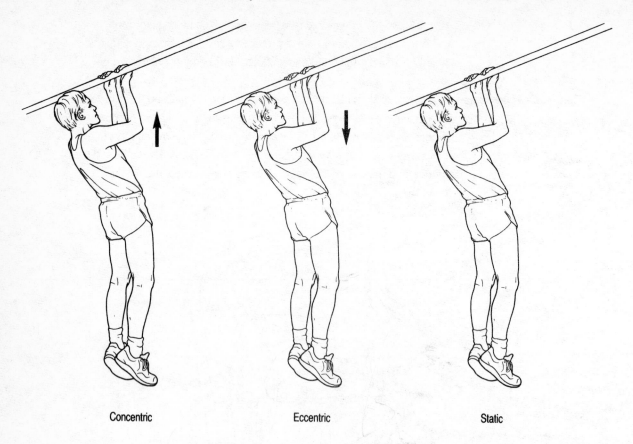

Concentric        Eccentric        Static

**concentrically**. An example is when an athlete attempts a 'pull-up' on an overhead bar. The biceps muscles contract and are shortened.

However, if an external force is exerted whilst the opposite ends of the muscle are moving away from each other, and the muscle is attempting to resist the force and shorten, then the muscle is working **eccentrically**. It is important to be aware that although the muscle attempts to shorten it is actually lengthened by the external forces. An example is the athlete slowly lowering themselves down from the pull-up bar.

When a muscle develops tension without any movement taking place at the joint, the muscular work is classified as **static**. For example, if you attempt to lift a piano by yourself, your arm muscles are contracting without causing movement. In these cases the electrochemical process that causes the filaments of the muscle to slide together takes place, but it fails to move the filaments. The muscle neither lengthens nor shortens.

**Muscle Shape**    Skeletal muscle is classified either by its shape or its function. In terms of shape, most skeletal muscles are one of two main types: pennate or strap shaped. On the **strap-shaped** muscles, the cells run longitudinally. These muscles are found where a large range of movement is required – for example, the stomach muscles (rectus abdominis). **Pennate** muscles are found where the required range of movement is small but great strength is required, such as in the thigh. The cells on the pennate muscles run diagonally in relation to the longitudinal direction of muscle.

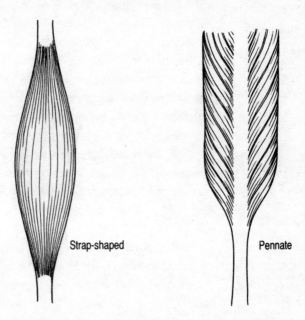

Strap-shaped                    Pennate

**Muscle Function**    All sports movements are the result of the co-ordinated action of many muscles. By stretching a muscle and developing its flexibility, one increases the range over which the muscle can move. An individual muscle, or group of muscles, may be classified by its function – that is, by the particular contribution they make to muscular movement. Muscles are considered as prime movers, antagonists, fixators or synergists, depending on the movements to which they are contributing at any one time.

A muscle is classified as a **prime mover** when it is the major muscle responsible for a particular movement. The thigh (quadriceps femoris) is a prime mover in the movement of extending the knee joint to kick a ball.

A muscle that opposes the action of a prime mover is an **antagonist**. The hamstrings (biceps femoris) oppose the action of the thigh (quadriceps femoris) when the knee is extended. Before the prime mover can contract, the antagonist must relax. A stiff or short antagonist muscle will inhibit the range of movement of its prime mover.

The **fixator** is a muscle that contracts without changing its length (static contraction) so that it can stabilize the prime mover. It thereby enables the prime mover to act efficiently. For example, the deltoid muscles in the shoulders are the prime movers in the action of putting the shot. The rhomboid major and minor muscles in the back act as fixators of the deltoids to the trunk muscles. Without strong fixators, putting the shot would be like trying to fire a cannon from a canoe.

A number of muscles cross several joints before they meet the joint at which the main action takes place. To prevent movement at the intermediate joints, other muscles contract and stabilize the intermediate joints. Muscles, when acting in this capacity, are called **synergists**.

The classification of a muscle as a prime mover or antagonist is specific to a particular muscle during a particular movement. The same muscle may fulfil different functions at different times. The action that a particular muscle performs during a particular movement is dependent on a number of factors, including the length of the muscle, the location of its origin and insertion, the joint that it covers, and its shape (pennate or strap). Some muscles and groups of muscles connect to more than one joint; for example, the hamstrings acts on the hip and knee joints. Therefore a muscle, or group of muscles, may have a number of different actions at different joints.

Finally, movements of the body can usefully be described as flexion, extension, abduction, adduction, rotation and circumduction. The illustrations below indicate these movements in the major limbs of the body.

- **Flexion** is a movement that decreases the angle formed at a joint. Flexion at the elbow produces a bend at the elbow.
- **Extension** is a movement that increases the angle formed at the joint. Extension of the elbow straightens the arm.
- **Abduction** is the movement of a segment of the body away from the mid-line of the body, as in doing astride jumps.
- **Adduction** is the movement of a segment of the body towards the mid-line of the body, as in the return phase of an astride jump.
- **Rotation** is the pivoting of a part of the body around its own axis. An example is turning the head to the right and then to the left.
- **Circumduction** is movement that permits a circle to be traced, as in circling your arms. It involves flexion, extension, abduction and adduction.

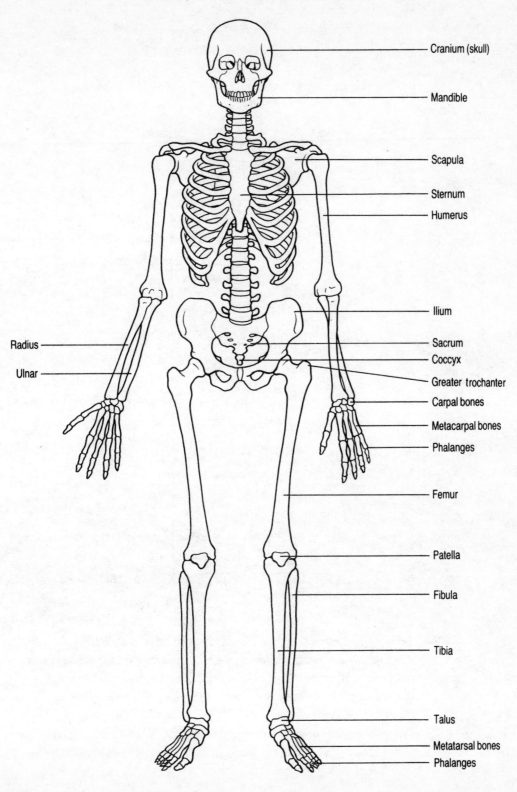

Cranium (skull)

Mandible

Scapula

Sternum

Humerus

Ilium

Radius

Sacrum

Coccyx

Ulnar

Greater trochanter

Carpal bones

Metacarpal bones

Phalanges

Femur

Patella

Fibula

Tibia

Talus

Metatarsal bones

Phalanges

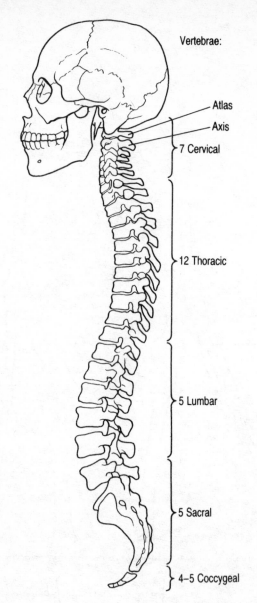

Vertebrae:

Atlas

Axis

7 Cervical

12 Thoracic

5 Lumbar

5 Sacral

4–5 Coccygeal

**Joints**  The point where two or more bones come together is a joint. A joint may provide either stability or mobility, depending upon its structure. The joints that are of most interest to sports people are those that provide mobility. These are primarily **synovial joints**, which are freely moving because there is space between the surface of the relevant connecting bones. A synovial membrane surrounds the joint and secretes a lubricating fluid. There are several types of synovial joints. They are classified either by the number of axes about which they rotate, or the number of planes within which they move. Joints are also named by their physical appearance, for instance the hinge joint of the ankle. The main joints include the ankle, knee, shoulder and hip.

The **ankle joint** is very important in running, walking and jumping. It permits movement mainly in one plane and is therefore considered **uniaxial**. In elite sprinters, one can clearly see a strong flexible movement of the foot downwards (plantar flexion). The major muscles involved (prime movers) are the gastrocnemius and soleus muscles of the calf. The opposite upward movement of the foot (dorsiflexion) towards the shins is primarily the responsibility of the tibialis anterior. The ankle joint is classified as a hinge joint as it resembles the hinge on a door. Unlike a real hinge, the ankle joint does permit very slight additional movements of rotation, abduction and adduction.

The **knee joint** is the largest in the human skeleton. It is supported by powerful ligaments and strong muscles. Despite these supporting structures it is relatively insecure, due to the poor arrangement of the connecting surfaces of the knee. The knee joint permits very little twisting (rotation). It is prone to injury in those sports that involve sudden changes in direction. Its movement is mainly flexion and extension. These movements are primarily controlled by the quadriceps and hamstring muscles. The knee joint is classified as a **uniaxial hinge joint**.

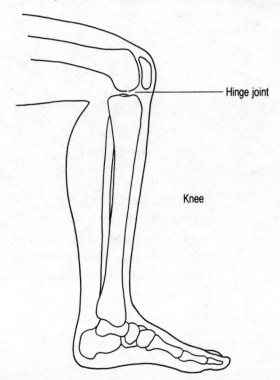

Hinge joint

Knee

The **shoulder joint** permits a great deal of movement in all directions. It is also relatively unstable due to its shallow shape and the particular arrangements of the surrounding ligaments. The shoulder joint relies mainly on strong muscles for stability. The various movements of the shoulder are controlled primarily by the deltoids, pectoralis major, infraspinatus, supraspinatus and latissimus dorsi. A typical injury to the shoulder is dislocation, which is due to the shallowness of the joint, the laxity of the associated ligaments and the weakness of the adjacent muscles. The shoulder joint is classified as a **multi-axial ball and socket joint**.

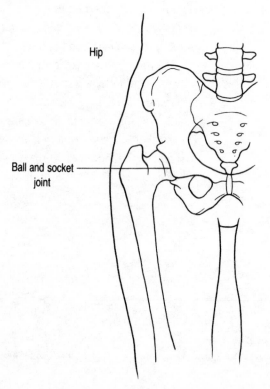

The **hip joint**, like the shoulder joint, is a ball and socket joint. Its range of motion is good, but not nearly as wide as the range in the shoulder. The round head of the femus bone fits into the cup of the pelvic bones. Unlike the shoulder joint, this fit is snug, so it is a stable joint and hip dislocations are rare. Several strong ligaments reinforce the stability of the hip joint.

*Joint Stability*  The stability of a joint is dependent on three main factors:

- the strength of the muscle around the joint;
- the ligaments; and
- the shape and size of the articular surfaces.

*Muscle Strength*  In most joints the strength of the associated muscle is a major factor in providing stability. For example, the knee joint is highly dependent on the thigh muscles (quadriceps femoris) to provide stability. Unstable knees are often associated with poor muscle tone. The muscles around the shoulder joint protect the head of the humerus from dislocating. The shallow cavity into which the humerus fits renders it susceptible to 'popping out' unless the adjacent muscle is in good condition.

*Ligaments*  Fibrous ligaments are tough, resistant and help to prevent most excessive movements in a joint. However, fibrous ligaments will stretch when subjected to continuous stress. The ligaments then become long and, if the muscles next to the joint lose their tone, the joint will become unstable.

*Articular Surfaces*  The arrangement of the bones making up a specific joint may contribute significantly to the stability of the joint. On page 14 we described the differences between the relative stability of hip joint and instability of the shoulder joint due primarily to the fit of the bones which form the joints.

## Limitations of Range of Motion

Flexibility is limited by anatomical, biophysical and neurophysiological factors. An understanding of these three areas will help explain the limitations of range of motion and the means of developing flexibility. **Anatomical** factors include bones, tendons, ligaments and joints. **Biophysics** is the study of biological structures and processes in connection with principles of physics. Factors affecting muscle and connective tissue include stress, relaxation and temperature. **Neurophysiology** looks at the reflex mechanism caused by stretching a muscle in a particular way.

**Anatomical Limitations**  Anatomically, flexibility is mainly limited by bone and joint structure, muscle, tendons, ligaments and joints.

The effect of ageing on bones and joints is a special consideration for the growing child and the older adult. During periods of rapid growth in childhood and adolescence there may be an increase in muscle and tendon tension and a reduction in flexibility because the bones are growing faster than the muscles are stretching. The opposite may also occur where muscle and connective tissue grow faster than the bones, leading to excessive mobility.

Two common bone diseases which can plague the older adult are osteoporosis and osteoarthritis. In both diseases, the bones become brittle and prone to injury. Osteoarthritis is one of the most common musculoskeletal problems in the older adult. The symptoms include aches, pains and stiffness in particular joints.

**Muscles** have amazing potential for lengthening and shortening. A muscle can shorten to 25–50 per cent of resting range when contracted, and when passively stretched the muscle may extend to over 150 per cent of its regular length.

However, the effect of ageing on muscle causes a reduction in strength, endurance and flexibility. The age at which these changes begin varies enormously depending on disease, injury and the amount of physical activity a person undertakes. The number of nerve cells in the musculoskeletal system reduces with age. Muscle cells atrophy, which reduces the size and number of cells. Fatty and fibrous tissue (collagen) then begins to replace muscle fibres. All of these changes in the muscle cause a reduction in flexibility. Regular stretching exercises throughout one's life can delay this part of the ageing process.

**Connective tissue** includes tendons, ligaments and fascia. There are two types of connective tissue that significantly affect flexibility. One type is fibrous tissue, which is mainly collagenous fibres; the other is elastic tissue consisting of elastic fibres. Collagen is strong and ridged and allows little movement, whereas elastic tissue can move and stretch.

**Tendons** attach muscles to bone and act to transfer tension to the bones, thereby facilitating movement. Tendons are thought to provide 10 per cent of total resistance to movement.

**Ligaments** bind bone to bone, holding the bones in place and thereby supporting the joints. Ligaments have a variety of shapes including bands, sheets and cords. They allow a certain amount of movement. It is estimated that they contribute as much as 47 per cent of total resistance to movement during passive motion.

Connective tissue, or **fascia**, makes up approximately 30 per cent of muscle mass. Fascia is the mesh of connective tissue that surrounds skeletal muscle. Muscle fascia accounts for 41 per cent of total resistance to movement during passive motion.

## Biophysical Limitations

To understand the factors that limit range of motion and the best methods of increasing flexibility, it helps to know something of the biophysics of muscle and connective tissue.

Two mechanical properties which are important include **creep** and **stress relaxation**. During a static stretch, where the position is held for a time at a constant length, there is a gradual reduction of tension. This is known as stress relaxation. The lengthening or increase in flexibility which occurs when a stretch is held is called creep.

**Temperature** has a significant effect on the behaviour of connective tissue. As the temperature of the tissue increases, resistance to movement decreases, and so the tissue can extend further.

Researchers have found that low force, long duration stretching causes permanent changes in flexibility. It is recommended that stretching is performed after warming up the muscles, although the best results are achieved when the tissue is allowed to cool by holding the stretch before withdrawing from it. This apparently helps the connective tissue to adjust to the new stretched length.

Low force stretching at higher temperatures leads to less structural weakening and damage than higher force stretching at lower temperatures. A warm-up, then, is essential in order to prepare the muscles for stretching.

## Neurological Limitations

There are two protective reflex mechanisms which are important in stretching muscles. These mechanisms involve muscle spindles and golgi tendon organs in their operation.

### Muscle Spindles

Muscle spindles consist of bundles of three to ten muscle fibres. The fibres are located in skeletal muscle and lie parallel to the muscle cells. Muscle fibres contain primary endings which are sensitive to both the velocity and length of stretch, and secondary endings which detect change in length.

Whenever a muscle is stretched, the muscle spindles are excited and the muscles and muscle spindles are lengthened. If the stretch is either too fast or too long, exceeding the threshold of the muscle spindles, the result will be a firing of the muscle spindles, which leads to the stretched muscle contracting due to the **stretch reflex**.

The dynamic nature of ballistic stretching, characterized by bouncing or jerky movements, is thought to invoke the stretch reflex, whereas slow, prolonged, static stretching is thought to overcome the influence of the stretch reflex contraction. However, an extreme static stretch, which exceeds the threshold of the muscle spindles, will result in the firing of the muscle spindles and cause the muscle to reflexively contract.

*Golgi Tendon Organs*  The golgi tendon organs (GTOs) are located in the tendon towards the end of the muscle fibres. They detect the amount of tension or strain in a tendon. Tendons attach muscle to bone and therefore the GTOs lie directly in line with the transmission of force from the muscle to the bone which causes movement. Tension monitored by the GTOs may be in the form of muscle contraction or muscle stretching.

Tension will occur when muscle fibres contract and pull on the tendon; this is immediately monitored by the GTOs. If the tension exceeds the threshold of the GTOs, they fire, causing an impulse to be transmitted to the spinal cord to inhibit the motor neurone in the muscle, resulting in the muscle reflexively relaxing so that the excessive tension is removed.

During the stretching of a muscle, most of the stretch is accommodated by the elastic muscle fibres, so the degree of tension on the tendon is not great in comparison to contraction. Therefore, only a very strong and extreme stretch will elicit an inhibitory response from the GTOs.

If the tension caused by a contraction or stretch exceeds the threshold of the GTOs, an immediate reflex occurs resulting in the muscle relaxing and the tension dissipating. The reflex is a safety device that prevents injury to muscles and tendons.

This reflex action may help explain the relaxation that occurs when a static stretch is held for a time towards the end of the range of motion (ROM). When the tension dissipates, it is possible to stretch the muscle further.

---

**The Body's Limitations**

- It has been estimated that muscle and fascia account for 41 per cent of total resistance to movement. Muscle and fascial sheaths are the only anatomical limiting factor which may be altered to give greater flexibility.

- Biophysical limitations reveal the importance of stress relaxation and creep in determining flexibility. Temperature has a significant effect upon mechanical behaviour. As the temperature of muscle increases, resistance to movement decreases, so extensibility becomes greater.

- The golgi tendon organs and muscle spindles are important structures which are involved in reflex mechanisms. These reflexes, to stretching or contraction, help explain the effectiveness of certain stretching methods, which are addressed more fully in the next section.

- Other factors which may affect the ROM at a joint include sex, age, the structure of a particular joint, exercise history, warm-up, temperature of the environment, time of day, and pregnancy. These factors will be considered in Part 3 of this book, 'Constructing a Flexibility Programme'.

The characteristic of the GTOs to detect tension caused by contraction may explain the muscular relaxation that occurs following contractions during proprioceptive neuromuscular facilitation (PNF) techniques.

## The Nature of Flexibility

There are two types of flexibility: static and dynamic. **Static flexibility** involves moving **slowly** into a stretching position and holding the body still. An example of extreme static flexibility is the ability to sit in the splits position.

**Dynamic flexibility** involves **speed**. It is the ability to use a range of movement at normal or rapid speed. An example in badminton is the overhead clear. In order to hit a successful shot, the player combines speed, strength, extreme shoulder extension, co-ordination and precision. Another example is a dancer or gymnast performing a split leap.

As flexibility is specific, static and dynamic flexibility are not necessarily related. For example, a dancer who can perform a sitting splits may not necessarily be able to execute a split leap. The dancer may lack sufficient strength in the appropriate muscles. Flexibility training must take this into account.

---

**About Flexibility**

- Flexibility is the range of motion (ROM) available in a joint or group of joints.
- Flexibility, or ROM, can be improved by performing stretching exercises.
- Flexibility is specific for each joint. Therefore the ROM in the shoulder is not necessarily similar to the ROM in the hip. The right and left side of the body often exhibit different ROM; the preferred side (usually the right side) is stronger and more flexible than the other side.
- Flexibility can be measured. It may be calculated either in linear units (centimetres or inches) or angular units (degrees).
- Poor or inadequate flexibility can lead to an increase in the risk of injury and may hamper performance. Extreme flexibility may also be a problem, as excessive flexibility without adequate amounts of strength may destabilize joints. In these cases, preventative and compensatory strength exercises are recommended to increase joint stability.
- Flexibility should be matched both to the individual and the sport or physical activity in which they participate. The flexibility needs of a ballet dancer are quite different to those of a rugby player.

## Methods of Stretching

There is a variety of stretching methods used by sportsmen and women to increase their flexibility. These stretching techniques may be classified as ballistic stretching, static stretching or proprioceptive neuromuscular facilitation (PNF).

**Ballistic** stretching involves using momentum or speed to stretch a muscle group. Small bouncing movements are applied at the extreme end of the movement range.

**Static** stretching is achieved by moving slowly into a stretching position towards the end of the range of movement, then holding the static position. A feeling of mild tension (not pain) should be felt in the muscle group being stretched.

**Proprioceptive neuromuscular facilitation** (PNF) techniques were devised by a physiotherapist, for the rehabilitation of paralytic patients. Further research found that the PNF method was also highly successful treating a wide variety of non-paralytic patients. PNF techniques were subsequently applied to various sports, notably gymnastics, where extreme flexibility is required for elite performance. Today, PNF is used as a stretching technique by many sportsmen and women to improve performance and reduce the chance of injury.

PNF includes a variety of techniques used for specific purposes. It may involve using isotonict (shortening and lengthening) and isometric (static) contractions in different combinations. For example, the hold–relax (HR) method begins with a maximal isometric contraction of the antagonist (target muscle being stretched) from a point of resistance against a partner, followed by a short period of relaxation. Then, the partner moves the body part to increase the range of movement as far as is comfortably possible. The process is then repeated.

There is much confusion over the definitions of PNF stretching techniques. A particular term may be used in books and in research papers to describe different techniques. Often the technique is not described in sufficient detail, leading to ambiguity. Authors may also modify techniques without alerting their readers, leading to further confusion. When reading a book or paper it is important to check the 'working definition' to be sure of the method intended.

The most commonly used stretching techniques for sport and dance are contract–relax, hold–relax and contract relax agonist contract.

**Contract–relax** (CR) involves a resisted concentric contraction (shortening) of the antagonists (the target muscles to be stretched), followed by relaxation then movement to increase flexibility.

**Hold–relax** (HR) involves a resisted isometric contraction (static) of the target muscles to be stretched (antagonists), followed by relaxation and then movement to increase flexibility.

**Contract–relax–agonist–contract** (CRAC) begins like the hold–relax technique, with an isometric contraction (static) of the target muscles to be stretched. The muscles then relax. This is immediately followed with a concentric contraction (shortening) of the opposing muscles (agonists), followed by relaxation and then movement to increase flexibility. (See 'PNF Partner Stretches' for a detailed description of HR and CRAC techniques.)

## Passive or Active?

An alternative way of describing stretching methods is to base the categories upon who or what is responsible for increasing the range of movement: the methods are called passive, active, passive–active and active–passive.

**Passive** stretching means that the individual being stretched does not contribute to the stretch. Rather, an outside agent (usually a partner) moves the body into a stretch position to lengthen the muscle concerned.

**Active** stretching is accomplished by the individual alone.

**Passive–active** stretching begins as a passive stretch, with a partner helping to move limb or body part towards the end of ROM. Then the stretcher attempts to maintain the stretch without assistance.

**Active–passive** stretching begins with the individual actively moving into a stretch position towards the end of ROM, as far as comfortably possible. At this stage a partner takes over, and moves the body part to complete the ROM available.

All of these methods may be performed in conjunction with static, ballistic and PNF stretching.

There is much controversy over which method of stretching most increases flexibility. There are also debates over the safest method; the most appropriate method for a specific sport or individual; and the method which produces the least amount of delayed onset of muscle soreness (DOMS).

Before deciding which method or methods are appropriate for any individual or sport, it is important to know the arguments for and against each stretching technique.

## Arguments for Ballistic Stretching

Research has indicated that ballistic and static stretching are equally effective in developing flexibility. However, contract–relax methods have been found to produce significantly higher increases in ROM in comparison to either ballistic or static stretching.

Ballistic stretching helps to develop dynamic flexibility. As many sports require dynamic flexibility, stretching ballistically is appropriate in some training. Many authors have recommended that ballistic stretching may have a place in preparatory stages of sport-specific rehearsal of movements.

Ballistic stretching has been favoured by some because it is more interesting than static stretching. Although this is not a scientific argument in favour of ballistic stretching, it is nevertheless important to consider the motivation of the individual.

### Arguments against Ballistic Stretching

Arguments against ballistic stretching include the problems of tissue adaptation, muscle soreness and the initiation of the stretch reflex. If a muscle is stretched quickly, the tissues are not given enough time to adapt to the change in length, so flexibility cannot be fully developed. In ballistic stretching, where bouncing is performed at the end of the movement range, the muscle continually changes length. This does not allow time for the mechanical properties of the muscle tendon unit (stress relaxation and creep) to operate.

It is generally agreed that ballistic stretching can cause soreness or injury. If a tissue is stretched too fast, it can be strained or ruptured, resulting in pain and often a reduction in ROM. Permanent lengthening is gained by lower force, longer duration stretches at elevated temperatures. Because there are much higher degrees of tension in ballistic stretching in comparison to static stretching, there is a greater likelihood of injury occurring.

The muscle spindles that initiate the stretch reflex are sensitive to both rate of stretch and excessive stretch. The stretch reflex is considered to be more easily provoked when the muscle is near its maximum length. Since ballistic stretching is characterized by small, fast bouncing movements towards the end of the range of motion, it is thought likely to invoke the stretch reflex on both accounts, which counteracts the benefits of the stretch.

### Arguments for Static Stretching

There is general agreement in popular literature that static stretching is preferable to ballistic stretching.

Firstly, static stretching is performed slowly, so the rate of stretch does not invoke a stretch reflex. Secondly, static stretching appears to cause less muscle soreness than other methods and is recommended by many professionals as an integral part of every warm-up and cool-down for this reason. Thirdly, static stretching has been shown to relieve muscle soreness. Recordings on an electromyocardiograph revealed that static stretching significantly reduced the electrical activity in the muscle. And lastly, because static stretching is performed slowly and held for a period of time, this allows the mechanical properties of the muscle tendon unit – stress relaxation and creep – to operate, thereby causing an increased lengthening in the muscle.

**Argument against Static Stretching**

There are very few arguments against static stretching. One criticism against static stretching is that it may be performed exclusively or at the expense of ballistic exercise. Some authors recommend an optimal blend of both static and ballistic exercise.

**Arguments for PNF**

Many researchers have found that PNF techniques produce the largest gains in ROM. During PNF, the maximal contraction is thought to invoke the golgi tendon organs, causing the muscle to relax. This would help explain the relaxation and ease of increasing the target muscle following contraction. **Successive induction** is either an isometric or an isotonic contraction of one muscle, followed immediately by a contraction of the opposing muscle. This is apparent in the CRAC technique, which is thought to promote strength as well as flexibility.

Other benefits of PNF (depending on the technique employed) include greater strength, balance of strength and stability surrounding a joint. Some authors report improved endurance and blood circulation. Enhanced co-ordination is also cited as a benefit. Finally, greater muscle relaxation is found with PNF techniques than with static or ballistic methods.

**Arguments against PNF**

PNF is an advanced technique, best introduced after a basic grounding in static stretching. It is most effective when performed with a partner, but it has been argued that it may be dangerous if the partner is not sensitive towards the stretcher's needs.

There are other arguments against performing PNF stretches. It has been reported that some PNF methods are painful and uncomfortable. Consequently some researchers find that PNF methods attract only well motivated individuals. Our personal experience has shown that athletes of all abilities have been willing to learn and perform PNF stretches.

Since PNF involves invoking tension in the muscle, it might be considered a more dangerous method in comparison to static stretching. PNF should be monitored more rigorously to avoid the risk of injury to soft tissue. The risk of injury is also present if PNF stretches are performed incorrectly – care should be taken whilst working with a partner.

Another disadvantage of using PNF is the possibility of the valsalva phenomenon (holding breath with a closed glottis) occurring, which elevates systolic blood pressure. Individuals with high blood pressure (hypertension) or a history of coronary artery disease may be at risk. It is important to exhale during intense isometric exercise and to breathe rhythmically and continuously throughout all exercise. **Do not hold your breath!**

***Which Stretch is Right?***

Static stretching is recommended as the basic method of maintaining and developing flexibility. It is advisable to perform static stretches during warm-up and cool-down. Static stretching improves ROM, provides relief from muscular soreness, and is regarded as a safe method of stretching.

Ballistic stretching is successful in developing ROM and some consider it a useful means of developing dynamic flexibility. We recommend that ballistic stretching should not be the basic or first method employed in warm-up. Rather, it should be used in sports and dance as a preparation for explosive movements. Ballistic exercises should be preceded by a slow, easy jog and/or mobility exercises and then static stretching. The ballistic method is performed at the end of the ROM and the small bounces serve to tone rather than stretch muscles, although it does increase the ROM. For example, towards the end of their warm-up a discus thrower will take the throwing arm backwards in line with the shoulder and then perform small bounces at the end of the ROM. A footballer just before kick off is often seen using ballistic stretching for the groin muscles, a common area of injury. The footballer performs a standing inner thigh lunge, then gently bounces in this position.

PNF is now regarded as the most efficient method for improving the ROM. Other benefits include enhanced co-ordination, superior relaxation of muscles and greater strength and joint stability. The most common PNF techniques used in sporting contexts are hold–relax (HR) and contract–relax–agonist–contract (CRAC). Contract–relax (CR) is another method that is sometimes used, though we feel that it is often difficult for a partner to control a concentric contraction of the antagonist (the stretched muscle).

**The authors recommend that PNF be used where ROM is poor.** Recommended techniques are HR and CRAC. In activities where extreme flexibility is desirable (for example some forms of dance, gymnastics, trampolining, diving, martial arts or ice dancing), the CRAC technique is advised. Some authors recommend that the partner's role should be to facilitate movements, rather than actively moving the body parts into the stretch position. In practice, we find that it is much more effective for the partner to have an active role. Partners should be sensitive to the flexibility needs of the stretcher, however, and should take care in following PNF procedures.

**Guidelines for Stretching**

To date there are no internationally agreed guidelines for the development of flexibility; there are still many questions that remain unanswered about flexibility development. Researchers need to identify the most effective application for each stretching method, allowing comparisons to be made between methods. Many existing studies focus on hip flexion, so future research could consider other joints. Research is also needed into the duration of a stretch and the number of consecutive repetitions and weekly frequency needed to maintain and develop a stretch. The guidelines we recommend here are based on existing research and practical experience.

**How long should a static stretch be held?** Recommendations from researchers and practitioners vary as much as 2 minutes! Of two recent studies on the duration of static stretching, one concluded that there were no significant differences in holding a stretch for 10, 20 or 30 seconds while the other reached the same conclusion on intervals of 15 or 45 seconds or 2 minutes. The two studies recommended 10 to 15 seconds respectively.

There are two static stretching techniques. The first involves moving slowly into a stretch, holding the position for a period of time and then returning to the starting position. The stretch may or may not be repeated. The second technique begins in the same way as the first by slowly moving into a stretching position, holding and relaxing. When the individual feels the tension subsiding in the stretched muscle, he or she moves a little further to increase the stretch, then again holds and relaxes. This is repeated as necessary. The whole process may take between 30 and 60 seconds.

**How long should the contraction aspect of PNF last?** Opinions on this differ, ranging between 5 and 10 seconds. Several researchers have found that 6 seconds is as good as any other duration in achieving gains in flexibility.

**How long does the effect of stretching last?** This will depend on the method and techniques employed. One researcher suggests that maximum extensibility following stretching can continue for at least 3 hours, with a small decline after 6 hours. Others advocate that the effects of stretching can last up to 48 hours. If athletes want to maintain their flexibility throughout a day-long competition, they can continually check their ROM in the joints concerned and use either static stretching or PNF to maintain flexibility.

**How many times per week should stretching exercises be performed?** Again this depends on the methods and techniques used. For PNF, at least three times per week has been recommended to develop flexibility and once a week to maintain it. For static stretching, every second day is often recommended to maintain flexibility; for development, daily stretching is usually advocated.

In terms of **frequency** of stretching, it is important to distinguish between stretching during a warm-up and stretching specifically to develop flexibility.

The athlete should be clear on his or her intentions when stretching. For example, a warm-up for most sports encompasses maintenance stretching. However, for some athletes it may be important to develop flexibility during the warm-up to enhance performance in sports like gymnastics or sprinting.

The following guidelines are recommended by the authors on the basis of research so far and their own practical experience. Like all guidelines, they remain open to possible review as future research uncovers the truth about stretching.

## Static Stretching

**Frequency**   3–5 times per week

**Duration**   **Maintenance or warm-up** Hold static stretch for 12–18 seconds, performing each stretch twice, 3 times per week
**Development** Hold static stretch for 12–18 seconds, performing each stretch 2–4 times, 5 times per week
OR
Hold static stretch and relax for 20–60 seconds or more, increasing the stretch each time a reduction in tension is experienced, 5 times per week

**Intensity**   Move into stretch position slowly, until mild tension is felt in the muscle being stretched. Stop, hold this position and relax the stretched muscle if possible

## PNF/Hold–Relax method

**Frequency**   **Maintenance** once per week
**Development** 3–5 times per week

**Duration**   Contract the antagonist (target muscle) for 6 seconds; relax muscle, holding the body in the stretched position for 4–6 seconds, and then (if comfortable), stretch the antagonist a little further. Depending on flexibility, repeat this twice more

**Intensity**   Move into a position of mild tension, stop and begin the PNF technique

## Measuring Flexibility

Most sportsmen and women subjectively assess their flexibility whilst performing static stretches. This is very useful to monitor positive or negative changes in flexibility. However, if the individual aspires to be (or is) an elite athlete, it would be useful to monitor flexibility alongside other physiological measures in a more scientific way.

**Why Test Flexibility?** Flexibility is tested to provide objective measurements, which can be monitored over a period of time. This information can stimulate and motivate the athlete. The coach may also use the information to help make decisions regarding performance or changes in the training programme. In some sports, physiological measurements are used in the selection of national squads or teams.

**Indirect methods** of testing generally involve linear measurement, either between segments of the body or from an object. The most popular method is the sit and reach test, usually done as a slow static stretch and hold. This involves the athlete sitting on the floor with both legs extended out in front and feet resting against the side of a bench. The athlete then leans forward with arms extended out in front, placing the hands on top of the bench and slowly reaching as far forward as comfortable, before stopping and holding the position. The distance reached is then measured on a scale on top of the bench.

This method is designed to measure both hamstring and back flexibility. Over the years the validity of this test has been questioned because of concern over the relationship between variable lengths of arms, legs and torso and performance on the sit and reach test. Results found that only a comparatively small number of subjects with outlying ratios of arm length to leg length are affected, so the sit and reach test has not been challenged. However, a study of the relationship of the sit and reach test to measures of hamstring and back flexibility found that the test has moderate validity when used as an assessment of hamstring flexibility, but appears not to provide a valid assessment of back, and in particular lower back flexibility. The subjects in this study were girls aged 13–15 years, so the results cannot be generalized to include females of other ages and males, but it is clear that more research is required on testing for flexibility.

**Direct methods** of testing flexibility used by physiotherapists include the goniometer, the Leighton flexometer, radiography and the electrogoniometer.

The goniometer is used to measure ROM at a joint in degrees. The centre of the goniometer is placed at the axis of rotation of the joint and the arms of the goniometer are aligned with the long axis of the bones of adjacent segments. Problems arise in identifying the axis of motion for complex actions and in positioning the arms of the goniometer along the bones of the segments.

Radiography has been recommended by some researchers to be the most valid way of measuring flexibility. Regardless of validity, however, this method is not practical because of the dangers of radioactive exposure, and the lack of access to equipment and to personnel qualified to operate it.

The electrogoniometer measures joint angles during activity, which sounds very promising for measuring dynamic flexibility. The electrogoniometer may well prove to be an excellent means of measuring flexibility, but currently more research and development is needed before it can be recommended for general use.

The Leighton flexometer is designed to directly measure the range of motion in degrees. The flexometer is basically a gravity needle that is strapped to the limb. The flexometer can measure ROM at several joints and for different joint actions. Research reveals that the Leighton flexometer is very reliable, which makes it a popular choice of instrument for measuring ROM.

---

### The Best Tests

- The indirect sit and reach method of testing is useful to gauge hamstring flexibility but it cannot be used to generalize the ROM in other joints in the body, since ROM is specific to each joint or group of joints.
- If more specific measures of flexibility are needed, then the Leighton flexometer seems to be the most reliable instrument for measuring ROM to date.
- There are factors which may affect the accuracy of the measurement, so as far as possible the testing protocol and testing environment should be the same for every test. For example, the external temperature of the laboratory or test area should be kept at the same level; a warm-up (including stretching exercises) should be standardized for all tests so that the muscle temperature of the athlete is elevated to roughly equal levels; and testing should take into account recent muscle activity – a hard training session the day before a test will possibly yield lower results than expected.

## Muscular Relaxation

Relaxation may be described as the ability to use energy efficiently and economically so that the minimum amount is expended for any given skill. Relaxation is an important aspect of skilled performance. An excellent performance of a golf swing or a gymnastics routine is characterized by ease of movement, perfect co-ordination, grace and apparent effortlessness. Relaxation is also regarded as a factor which helps reduce the onset of fatigue, thereby reducing the risk of injury.

**Relaxation during Stretching Exercises**

Ideally the target muscle should be as relaxed as possible prior to moving into the stretch position. This means that there will be a minimum amount of tension in the muscle, so that when the individual moves slowly into the stretch position the connective tissue is able to stretch more effectively.

**Static Stretching**

In static stretching, the athlete moves slowly into a stretch position towards the end of the ROM and stops at the point where mild tension is experienced in the muscle group. This position is then held for 12–18 seconds. During this time the tension in the target muscle is reduced and relaxation is felt.

The causes of muscle relaxation may be explained in the following theories. Firstly, the stretch receptors (muscle spindles) in the muscle, which monitor length and speed of stretch, become desensitized to the held static stretch. As a result they make adaptations, neutralizing the stretch reflex. Secondly, if the tension caused by the static stretch is strong enough, the golgi tendon organs will be activated, reducing the tension in the muscle. Thirdly, the time-dependent mechanical properties of muscle and connective tissue may hold the key to explaining why relaxation is induced in a held static stretch. When a constant force is applied, there is a progressive change in length of the muscle and reduction in tension, which leads to stress relaxation and a decrease in the discharge of muscle spindle firing.

**PNF Stretching**

This method of stretching is successful because relaxation is induced following a contraction and the target muscle is easily able to increase the stretch. In the hold–relax technique, a muscle or limb is moved slowly towards the end of the ROM until further movement is prevented by tension in the target muscle. At this point an isometric contraction is performed by the target muscle. This causes the golgi tendon organs to fire, initiating the autogenic inhibition which induces relaxation in the muscle. With the cessation of the isometric contraction and the effect of the autogenic inhibition, the muscle undergoes a double dose of relaxation which easily allows the muscle or limb to increase the length of the stretch, thereby increasing the ROM.

## Methods of Inducing Relaxation

There are a variety of methods which can induce relaxation. Some of these methods can be performed by a layperson whilst others must be performed by qualified personnel, usually a physiotherapist.

### Breath Control

Breathing can be voluntary or involuntary. It involves taking air into the lungs (inhalation) and then expelling air (exhalation). By controlling and slowing down the rate of breathing, tension can be reduced, thereby increasing relaxation. In sports where accuracy is of prime importance – such as archery or rifle shooting – it is vital that the body is relaxed.

Breathing should be continuous and relaxed throughout all stretching exercises. It is particularly important that the breath is not held during PNF contractions. During stretching exercises, it is useful to use exhalation to increase the ROM. Move the muscle or limb slowly into a stretch towards the end of the ROM. Stop and hold this position for several breathing cycles. Then during subsequent exhalations, increase the stretch until tension is again felt, then repeat the sequence again.

### Progressive Muscular Relaxation

Progressive relaxation was devised by Edmund Jacobsen in 1938. Usually the subject lies on the floor on their back, with legs extended and arms by sides. The subject statically contracts a particular muscle group, then releases the tension. This highlights the difference between tense and relaxed muscles. The subject repeats this sequence in a systematic order from head to feet, or feet to head, gradually relaxing the entire body.

The aim of using progressive muscular relaxation is to transfer the skill learned above to real-life situations. It is a useful tool in many sporting and exercise contexts.

### Heat

The use of heat is a common method to help relieve pain and muscular tension. Hot baths, saunas, jacuzzis, hot water in bottles and packs, and electric heating pads are all ways of using heat to induce relaxation. However, if you are suffering from a serious injury, seek advice from a GP or physiotherapist regarding the most appropriate method of treatment.

### Massage

Massage is the manipulation of body tissues to benefit the nervous and muscular system and improve general circulation. Massage may be performed by a physiotherapist or layperson, provided they have a practical understanding of the movements involved. If, however, you are suffering from a serious injury, seek the advice and attention of a physiotherapist.

There are four basic types of movement used in massage:

- **Effleurage** – Stroking movements that may be superficial or deep and should be administered in a slow, gentle, rhythmic fashion. This method encourages the flow of venous blood and lymph.
- **Petrissage** – Kneading and squeezing movements that aim to treat adhesions in the muscle. The degree of pressure will depend on the condition of the tissues.
- **Friction** – Intended to treat the underlying muscles, usually with small circular movements. Deep pressure is often applied in order to affect the deeper muscles.
- **Tapotement** – Vibratory movements, such as hacking, clapping, beating or drumming, shaking or boating, which are used to stimulate the muscle tissue.

Massage is particularly useful for speeding up recovery from muscle soreness and fatigue.

## Analgesics and Counterirritants

Analgesics and counterirritants are commonly used by athletes in the treatment of muscular aches and pains.

Oil of wintergreen, peppermint and camphor are counterirritants that are rubbed into the skin. They act as mild irritants that help mask the muscular pain. The oils cause the blood vessels to dilate and the muscle fibres surrounding the blood vessels to relax. This increase in circulation aids the absorption of inflammatory products and brings more blood and nutrients to the affected area.

Analgesia is the absence or reduction of pain whilst maintaining consciousness. Usually we think of drugs like aspirin, ibuprofen or paracetamol, but analgesic rubs using oils can be effective in relieving muscular pain. Both analgesics and counterirritants are most effective for relatively superficial soft tissue injuries.

## Diathermy

Diathermy might be described as deep heating and must be prescribed and administered by physiotherapists. There are three main types – short wave, microwave and ultrasound. These methods of treatment increase the flow of blood in the muscle being treated, increase tissue metabolism, decrease sensitivity of the muscle spindles and induce muscular relaxation. Afterwards the tissue is more able to stretch.

***Cryotherapy***    Cryotherapy uses cold for therapeutic purposes. The cold acts as an anaesthetic, effectively promoting relaxation and helping to relieve pain in the muscle.

Cryotherapy is used to relieve pain only when no other ROM therapy can be administered because of the intensity of the pain and muscle spasticity. The aim of this treatment is to tear connective tissue rather than stretch it in order to relax the muscle, reduce pain and later increase ROM.

---

**Successful Relaxation**

- Relaxation is very important in relation to successful stretching.
- If a particular stretching position is uncomfortable and causes the target muscle to be tense, it is unlikely that the athlete will receive any benefit from stretching in this position. Instead another stretching position should be sought for the same muscle group.
- Special attention should be paid to the breathing throughout stretching exercises, making sure that it is slow and continuous.
- Muscular relaxation can be induced or facilitated through a variety of methods. Some methods can be performed by the athlete, whilst others must be prescribed and administered by a physiotherapist.

| # Understanding Injuries

## Reasons for Injuries

Sports injuries are not an act of fate. Simple methods of prevention will avoid most problems. However, the more frequently you participate in sport and exercise, the greater are the chances that you will incur an injury at some stage. You will need expert and sympathetic advice in order to cure the problem, to prevent a repetition and to return you to participation as quickly as possible.

The key to successful treatment is to understand the cause of the injury, and then to **treat the cause**, not the symptom. In order to find the cause of injury you will need to visit a doctor or physiotherapist who is sympathetic to sports people. It is rarely worth going to a doctor who has not played sport or been trained in sports medicine. Standard medical training normally places a low priority on understanding sports injuries and has inevitably produced doctors with little insight into the causes of many injuries.

If you are injured you should consider the nature of the problem yourself. Have you had the problem before? If so, did you manage the injury successfully? Why has it returned? You know your body better than anybody else, so do not undervalue your own knowledge and experience. But it is only the most experienced of athletes who can diagnose their own injuries. Even these individuals will usually require the assistance of a skilled physiotherapist.

If you cannot deal with the injury yourself, then go to a sports injury clinic. If there is no sports injury clinic nearby, go to an experienced coach in your sport and ask their advice as to the best local facility or individual. If these avenues fail, go to your general practitioner.

**Types of Injury**  Injuries are divided into two groups: traumatic and overuse. **Traumatic** injuries are those that are sudden and felt immediately, such as a blow received from a squash racquet, a fall from a bike or a pulled hamstring. **Overuse** injuries are more subtle. They are usually the result of repetitive movements over a period of time; for instance, sore elbows in tennis players, or sore shins in runners. They tend to start as a minor discomfort and deteriorate into pain if untreated.

Doctors are usually more comfortable dealing with a traumatic injury because the cause of the problem is normally clear.

Bruises, cuts and breaks have very obvious causes. The necessary therapy will be indicated by the tissue damage, not the fact that the injury occurred through sport. However, some traumatic injuries have a less obvious cause, as in the rupture of the Achilles tendon in squash players. In these cases a sports injury specialist is required if the rehabilitation process and future preventative measures are to be successful.

Finding the cause of overuse injuries is often very difficult, as there can be a combination of factors contributing to the problem. An accurate diagnosis often requires a knowledge of how the body moves within the framework of the sport. An accurate diagnosis is essential if the appropriate treatment is to be applied.

Overuse injuries are normally caused by the interaction of three factors: genetic endowment, training methods and training environment. Whilst you can do nothing about your genes, the other two factors are under your control.

## Factors Influencing Injury

**Genetic Endowment**  The genetic factors that may contribute to injury are usually associated with the shape and symmetry of your body. If your sport involves running, the following conditions may predispose you to problems: bow legs, short leg syndrome, knock knees or flat feet. Most people will have a tendency to one of these conditions; some may be afflicted by more than one. These abnormalities interfere with the placement of the foot as it strikes the ground. Most of us are stuck with feet which roll either too much or too little as they try to counteract the minor asymmetries of the leg. Your physical structure in the lower limbs can lead to knee pains and Achilles tendon problems.

If you are troubled with continuous knee and Achilles pain, do not despair. Whilst you may not have the best lower limb structure in the world, help is at hand. Most sports injury clinics will have a podiatrist that they can recommend. A podiatrist will be able to assess your biomechanical structure and provide you with inserts, or **orthotics**, for your shoes. These devices compensate for nature's shortcomings and enable you to run without pain. It will normally take two to three weeks for you to 'run in' these devices but they can banish your leg problems forever. Many athletes have had their athletic careers rescued by visiting a podiatrist.

**Training Methods**

Inadequate training methods are a major cause of injury in many sports. Most sportspeople spend their training sessions on skills practice or team strategy. They either neglect, or pay lip service to, fitness. Cricketers, for example, will spend hours in the nets practising their batting technique. However, practising batting skills does not prepare you for all of the physical demands of batting. A vital part of batting, the sprint for a swift single run, is often neglected. Batsmen frequently injure hamstrings and tendons attempting a short single, as they are not prepared for the intensity of the exercise required to sprint quickly. Similarly, fielders injure shoulders when they try to throw the ball over distances, and at speeds, with which they are unfamiliar.

Lack of **endurance** can result in injury. Tired players will attempt to make moves that are beyond their physical capacity, resulting in damage to muscle. Fatigue also has a disastrous effect on co-ordination. A mistimed tackle in football, for example, is dangerous at any point in a match. The chances of tired players mistiming tackles is significant. The better your endurance, the longer you can play before fatigue sets in and the quicker you can recover between efforts.

**If you wish to minimize the risk of injury, get fit and stay fit!**

If you train frequently for one sport you run the risk of developing a limited group of muscles and neglecting other muscles. Distance runners, for example, tend to have strong thigh (quadriceps) muscles and relatively weak hamstrings. Proper training methods emphasize **balanced muscular development**. Elite distance runners will include strength training and stretching in their training programmes to counteract the one-sided development caused by running. Similarly, playing sports such as tennis, golf, badminton and squash will develop one side of the body. An appropriate training programme that stresses flexibility and strengthening will rectify the imbalance.

**Flexibility training** will enable you to achieve balance in your muscles so that no group becomes abnormally tight and prone to injury. It will also increase your ROM, which will improve your technique.

Recent research has shown that in contact sports such as football, rugby and hockey, the frequency of injury is associated with the frequency of playing matches. The more matches people play, the more injuries they receive. It is probable that part of the reason for the rate of injuries is that playing matches on a twice-a-week basis, or even a weekly basis, leaves little time to pursue fitness. **Remember that playing the game does not prepare you for all the fitness requirements of the game**.

So you need to analyse your sport and decide what physical qualities it requires. It is useful to consider the qualities under the headings of endurance, strength, speed, flexibility, co-ordination, technique and muscular balance. With the help of an experienced coach, work out a gentle, progressive training schedule for each quality relevant to your sport.

## Training and Competition Environment

The third factor associated with sports injuries is the training and competition environment. An unsafe environment creates safety hazards which are responsible for many traumatic injuries. The way to avoid traumatic injuries is to minimize the risk factors.

Check your equipment. Shoes should have plenty of cushioning; studs and spikes should be the correct length and type for the conditions; safety gear should be worn (shin pads, helmets, boxes etc). Check the playing venue. Is the floor safe? Are the landing mats in the correct position, secure and at the correct height? If there are any shortcomings in the venue insist they are rectified **before you play**. If the problems cannot be resolved, **do not play**. Do not compromise on your safety. One international high jumper agreed to jump with an inadequate landing mat at an international competition. She landed on the edge of the mat and damaged ankle ligaments so severely that she was never able to compete again.

## How to Avoid Injury

The golden rules for avoiding injury are:

- Be fit for your sport;
- Check your kit and equipment for wear and tear;
- Check the competition and training environment for hazards;
- Always warm up and cool down;
- Allow your body time to adapt to higher levels of training.

You can avoid injuries by allowing your body time to adapt to the sport and the stress of training. If you have had a break from training in the close season, do not start your pre-season training by doing a tough session. The first session should be easy jogging and stretching with a little skill training.

Do not make any **sudden changes** to your training routine. If you are training for football twice each week, do not increase to five times the next week. Add one session each week. Runners should not increase their weekly mileage by more than 16 kilometres (10 miles) a week. Alternate hard training sessions with easy sessions. Do not attempt two tough training sessions on consecutive days. The body is a wonderful machine but it needs time to adapt to training.

You must **warm up** before each session of exercise. A warm-up prepares you mentally and physically for the challenge of the exercise session.

At rest, the blood flow in the muscles is relatively low and most of the vessels supplying them are closed. Only about 15–20 per cent of the total blood volume is directed to the muscles. After 10 or 12 minutes of jogging, the figure is about 70–75 per cent. As your physical performance in most sports is dependent on having an adequate supply of blood to your muscles, a warm-up is essential in assisting you to achieve your potential.

A warm-up prevents injury because it raises the temperature of muscle. The warmth is thought to increase the elasticity of muscle tissue, so that warmed-up muscles stretch to a greater length before tearing. There is a similar effect on tendons and ligaments.

You will find specific advice on warm-up in Part 5, which deals with particular sports. Generally, a warm-up comprises four sections: jogging to raise the temperature of the muscles; stretching to increase the range of movement of the muscles; mobilizing exercises to loosen joints; and skill rehearsal. The warm-up will take at least 15 minutes.

Older people tend to be less active in everyday life than younger people. Consequently muscles and tendons will shorten due to inactivity. Older people are therefore more at risk of overstretching their muscles during exercise unless they complete a thorough warm-up.

The **cool-down** after activity is also important as it tends to reduce the muscular stiffness that follows rigorous exercise. It is thought that the stiffness is due to the 'pooling' of the waste products of exercise in and around the muscles. If you suddenly cease vigorous exercise, the heart stops pumping large quantities of blood around the body and the waste products remain trapped in the muscle. By stopping exercise gradually, and slowly reducing the intensity at which you are working, you can assist these waste products to dissipate.

The most effective cool-down is 5 to 10 minutes of light aerobic exercise on a stationary bike, rowing machine or jogging machine at an intensity that enables you to talk without being out of breath. It is also advantageous to stretch the muscles that have been most active during your exercise session when cooling down.

## Responding to Injury

Most injuries to muscles are strains, tears and ruptures of the muscle fibres. It will take an expert in sports injury treatment to distinguish the severity of the problem. Fortunately the principles of treatment are similar in all but the most extreme cases.

**First Aid for Muscle Injuries**

**The treatment that you receive within the first 24 hours of sustaining a muscle injury is very important.** The correct treatment will enhance your chances of a speedy and complete recovery. The wrong treatment will slow your recovery and may lead to complications.

When a muscle is strained it releases fluid in and around the site of the injury. The fluid may be either a clear substance or blood. The presence of fluid causes swelling, pain and sometimes bruising and discolouring of the skin. First aid treatment for muscle strains aims to limit the amount of swelling, pain and bruising. The treatment is known by the acronym RICE – Rest, Ice, Compression, Elevation.

**Rest** the injured muscle. If you exercise the muscle it is likely to add to the amount of fluid and blood that gathers at the site of the injury, which will increase the bruising and slow the healing process.

Apply **ice** or cold water to the injured muscle as soon as possible after the incident that caused the injury. If you are in a sports centre ask at the reception desk for ice. **Do not delay!** Cold treatments (cryotherapy) are the best and easiest method for relieving pain, controlling swelling and reducing internal bleeding. Use an ice pack, ice cubes or a towel which is soaked in cold water. Even a pack of frozen food will do. Throw the pack away after use or label it. Do not consume the contents! Apply ice for 10 or 15 minutes every couple of hours throughout the first 48 hours following the injury.

It is unwise to apply ice directly to the skin as the cold can cause irritations. You may need to apply some baby oil first if your skin is sensitive. Alternatively, wrap the ice in a clean handkerchief or thin cloth before placing it on to the skin. If the ice is still too cold, simply dab the ice onto the skin until there is mild reddening of the area.

**Do not apply heat to the muscle** in the first 48 hours of the injury. If you take a hot shower or bath, avoid letting the water touch the injured muscle. Heat stimulates blood flow and tends to increase swelling in an injury. Heat treatments become relevant in later stages in the management of muscle injuries.

**Compression** is recommended at the first aid stage of treatment. A small firm bandage applied to the muscle helps to control swelling. Caution should be exercised when applying the bandage. It should not be so tight that it acts as a tourniquet and reduces circulation to the rest of the limb.

Finally, raise the injured limb whenever you sit down. Raising the limb will use gravity to minimize the accumulation of fluid around the injury. Gravity assists the fluid to move downwards whilst restricting the flow in the opposite direction. **Elevating** the injured muscle minimizes swelling. At night, you can place some books under your mattress to achieve elevation.

If there is still pain after 48 hours, you will need expert help. You should:

- Obtain an accurate diagnosis from a sport injury specialist;
- Carefully follow the recommended rehabilitation programme;
- Regain full range of movement through active static stretching and appropriate mobility exercises;
- Regain strength through resistance exercises; and
- Maintain endurance through aerobic exercise.

**Training during Injury**
Many doctors will advise complete rest for the injured person. These doctors are out of touch with the physical and psychological needs of sports people. It is very rare that an injury will prevent you from training in some form or another. Remember, **exercise is a critical part of your rehabilitation**. By continuing to exercise, you will maintain your fitness whilst your injury is healing. Consequently, when your injury allows you to return to full training or competition, you will be in good condition. You will then be less likely to immediately suffer another injury due to low fitness levels.

Exercise programmes can include any form of activity that does not cause you pain at the site of the injury. Cycling and swimming are excellent sports for maintaining condition.

Recent research has shown that pool running or **aqua running** is an outstanding form of exercise for injured sports people. Borrow a wet vest from your nearest sports injury clinic. The vest is a buoyancy aid that will keep you upright in the pool. You should then go to the deep end of your local swimming pool and try to run as you would on dry land. Simply repeat your normal training session but in the pool. If you normally run for 20 minutes, try to do the same. If you are scheduled to do an interval session (eg four or five fast runs with rest periods), do the same on your aqua run.

Aqua running has been shown to preserve endurance and leg strength, burn calories and maintain fitness. If you can run in the water without a wet vest, so much the better. Studies show that aqua running without a vest produces greater fitness gains than running with one. However, you will need to be fairly buoyant to manage without the vest.

In the Appendix, you will find an analysis of the most common sites of injury as reported by the University of Edinburgh Sports Injury Clinic.

## PART 3

**Constructing a Flexibility Programme**

## Individual Flexibility

There are a number of considerations to take into account when devising an individual flexibility programme.

- How much flexibility is appropriate for the particular sport in question?
- What level is the athlete currently playing at and what are their ambitions?
- What is their current flexibility and what idiosyncrasies do they possess?
- Have they ever been injured and if so, why?

These are just some of the questions that need to be asked so that the flexibility programme is informed of the past and present history of an individual and in line with aspirations and proposed training schedules.

**Requirements of the Sport** The ROM required differs radically from one sport to another. Flexibility should be considered alongside the other physiological requirements for the sport, including aerobic and anaerobic fitness, speed, muscular strength and endurance. For example, the flexibility needs of a dancer are quite different to those of a hockey player. The elite dancer needs extreme flexibility, especially in outward rotation of legs and hamstring and adductor muscles. However, the dancer also requires a certain amount of strength in order to move the body using the end of the ROM. For example, if a dancer from a standing position lifts the right leg up as high as possible in front of the body to the end of the ROM, not only does this require extreme flexibility of the hamstrings but also strength in the quadriceps to lift the leg to the desired position. Extreme flexibility without adequate strength will limit performance.

A hockey player requires above average but not extreme levels of flexibility, so that there is ease of movement in all possible body positions. This above average level of flexibility will also act as an insurance policy against the risk of injury. In the context of other physiological requirements, an elite hockey player will have very high levels of aerobic and anaerobic fitness, high levels of muscular endurance, above average levels of muscular strength and flexibility.

**The Ability of the Athlete**

The current level of the athlete is another important consideration when discussing flexibility. Is the athlete a beginner, intermediate, advanced or elite performer? Are they currently performing at a recreational, national or international standard? Are they amateur or professional? Are they a full-time, part-time or spare-time athlete?

The current level of participation is important but the potential and aspirations of the athlete must also be taken into account when developing a flexibility programme.

**The Athlete's Age**

The age of the athlete is of prime importance to flexibility since the muscles begin to lose their extensibility properties as we get older. Infants and children are naturally flexible, but as we get older we tend to lose ROM. There have been several studies on the flexibility of girls and boys at certain ages. These results for girls reveal some trends in relation to age, with a gradual increase in flexibility from ages 6 to 12 and then a gradual decline in flexibility with the onset of puberty. Similar studies with boys show a gradual increase in flexibility from ages 6 to 10 and then a gradual decrease during adolescence.

Advancing age means that muscle elasticity decreases though contractibility remains; often the amount of physical activity is decreased. Maintenance of, or an increase in, physical activity – including stretching exercises – can keep the effects of ageing to a minimum.

Veteran events are increasing in many sports. The older participant should spent time before and after training and competitions performing stretching exercises to maintain current ROM and increase ROM where necessary.

**Gender Differences**

Generally, women are more flexible than men and remain so throughout life. The shape of the pelvis helps to explain why women have greater potential for range of motion. The female pelvis differs from that of a male in the qualities that make it better adapted to childbearing. The female pelvis is wider, more like a cylindrical shape, shallower and shorter; the bones are both lighter and smoother, the coccyx more moveable and the angle of the pubic arch more acute. Consequently, the heads of the bones are further apart in women. Broader hips give women a greater potential for ROM. Therefore splits and high extensions are easier for women to perform.

The gender differences in sports participation during childhood and adolescence can also have an effect on flexibility. Traditionally boys played sports like football, cricket and rugby while the girls danced and took part in gymnastics. Recently these traditional sporting stereotypes have become blurred with an increase in female participation in male dominated sports such as rugby and football. However, this increase is small and with the upsurge of aerobic classes in the 1980s, predominantly populated by females, the gender differences in sporting opportunities and participation are still poles apart. Therefore gender differences in sports participation is still a significant variable for flexibility.

## Current Flexibility

Current flexibility depends on heredity and on what forms of sport and stretching the athlete has done thus far. Some people are simply born with greater potential for developing flexibility than others. Some people may never be able to touch their toes from a sitting position with both legs extended out in front. Fortunately, it is not necessary for everyone to aspire to the extreme flexibility that is only important at elite level in some forms of dance and sports such as gymnastics, trampolining and martial arts.

The forms of sport that we participate in during childhood and adolescence can have an affect on our current levels of flexibility. Sports and activities which include stretching as part of the warm-up process or demand high levels of flexibility in order to achieve good results promote an increase in ROM that seems to last into early adulthood. Traditionally participants in sports such as football, rugby and hockey, which do not require high levels of flexibility, did not bother much with warm-up or stretching; consequently, participants developed good muscular strength and endurance but little flexibility. Today, there is much more appreciation of the benefits of a warm-up (including stretching exercises) for all sporting activities, so the disparity in ROM between sports should be less.

## Individual Idiosyncrasies

It is important to know if the athlete has any idiosyncrasies that might affect their performance. For example, it is fairly common for there to be a difference in flexibility between the right and the left side of the body. If there is a difference, but the sport in question is also asymmetric (such as golf, discus or javelin), it may not hamper elite performance. If the sport is sprinting, gymnastics or diving, then a difference in flexibility between the right and left side may mar elite performance.

Another idiosyncrasy is the difference in leg or arm length between left and right sides. Again this is reasonably common, but it is only a problem if it causes discomfort or injuries. If this is the case, a podiatrist could be consulted to diagnose the problem and arrange treatment, often in the form of orthotics.

**Previous Injuries**

It is useful to know the case history of all injuries and if there has been any recurrence. Areas of past injuries should be treated with care and every warm-up should pay special attention to the area in question.

**Training and Competitive Schedule**

The competitive season has implications for designing a flexibility programme for an athlete. Sports such as football, hockey and athletics operate on a seasonal basis. Therefore in building up a profile on an athlete it is wise to understand the pattern of competition.

Training may take on different forms, depending on which part of the competitive cycle the athlete is at. Training may include developing or maintaining aerobic fitness, anaerobic fitness, muscular strength and endurance and flexibility. Flexibility is the one component which should be worked on at every training session, whether on a maintenance or developmental basis, in order to reduce the risk of injury and aid in ease of performance.

**Time constraints**

What are the time constraints on the athlete? Are they training full-time, part-time or in their spare time? Are they studying full-time, either at school or university? What are the other time constraints? Are they married or single, do they have any children?

It is vital to know how much time an athlete has to train. The higher the ambition, the higher the stakes in terms of training. A flexibility programme should be devised in consultation with the athlete and coach so that it blends into the other physiological aspects of training.

**Psychological Preparation**

Psychological preparation is important for all sports. This may take the form of a number of procedures and practices, including development of arousal level, concentration and attention, and motivation. Pre-competition psychological preparation may be performed in the warm-up during the static stretches, which lend themselves to reflection and concentration on mental rehearsal. Psychological preparation is an individual matter; there is no magic formula that will work for everyone.

**Time of Day**

When designing a flexibility programme in conjunction with other aspects of conditioning, it is important to know the time of day that the athlete is training. For example, we are at our stiffest first thing in the morning, but many athletes train then. This is generally due to a time constraint on the athlete but occasionally depends on the availability of facilities such as swimming pools.

If the athlete is training twice a day (as many elite athletes do), one session will generally be in the morning and one in the afternoon or evening. An athlete training in the morning should take care to warm up properly, using appropriate stretching exercises to safeguard against the risk of injury. As the day progresses, we generally feel more flexible. A hot shower or bath increases the ROM in our joints.

**Day to Day**

Flexibility can vary from day to day as well as within a particular day. For example, after a hard training session the ROM may decrease. This may also be accompanied by delayed onset muscle soreness (DOMS) which appears to peak 24 hours after exercise. In contrast, after a good quality stretching session, ROM is at a peak.

**Temperature of the Environment**

An increase in temperature, either in the weather or direct heat in a room, can increase the elasticity of muscles and consequently the ROM. The opposite is also true, so warm-up and stretching exercises prior to sports such as skiing, curling and ice dancing are vital. All athletes who train outdoors in the winter in cold climates should pay particular attention to warming up and stretching before training.

**Pregnancy**

Several elite women athletes have continued to train during pregnancy and have achieved success at the highest levels in their sport in the years following pregnancy. Examples are Liz McColgan and Lisa Ondieki.

With regard to flexibility, there are some precautions to take during pregnancy. The hormone relaxin is released during pregnancy, which causes the ligaments to relax in preparation for the birth of the baby. Therefore it is important not to take advantage of the laxity in the ligaments, since a lengthening of the ligaments may cause joint instability. Flexibility should be maintained and not developed during pregnancy.

## INADVISABLE EXERCISES

There are a number of exercises which may be categorized as inadvisable because they are potentially dangerous and may cause injury. There is always a safer and more effective alternative.

EXERCISE **1**  **Neck stretches**

Hyperextension of the neck region may cause compression damage to discs, vertebrae or nerves.

*Safe alternatives*
   Mobility 6 **Neck rotation**
   Mobility 7 **Neck side flexion**

EXERCISE **2**  **Neck circles**

The posterior movement of neck circles is at the least uncomfortable for most people and may cause damage to the cervical spine. It is often performed very quickly in some forms of dance, notably jazz dance. This is a common warm-up exercise which should be avoided.

*Safe alternatives*
Mobility 6 **Neck rotation**
Mobility 7 **Neck side flexion**

EXERCISE **3**  **Plough**

The aim of this position is to stretch the cervical section of the spine, but with the weight of the body balanced on the neck, it is not surprising that this exercise should be avoided. It is a yoga position and very flexible individuals can hold the stretch, but it places the neck under considerable stress.

*Safe alternative*
Mobility 8 **Forward neck flexion**

EXERCISE **4** **Bridge**

The bridge position places considerable strain on the vertebrae. It is a functional requirement in Olympic gymnastics and modern rhythmic gymnastics; participants in these sports require extreme flexibility. It is not, however, a desirable exercise for any other sport or for less flexible individuals.

*Safe alternatives*

Mobility 1 **Back extension**

Static stretching 24 **Pelvic tilt**

EXERCISE **5** **Banana bends**

Banana bends performed with limbs extended or hands grasping ankles should be avoided. Banana bends are a very poor mobility exercise. Again the problem is hyperextension of the spine, causing compression of the vertebrae, discs and nerves. The added weight of the arms and legs on the back may cause damage to the lower back muscles when lowering to the floor from the hyperextension position.

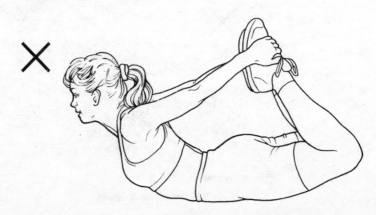

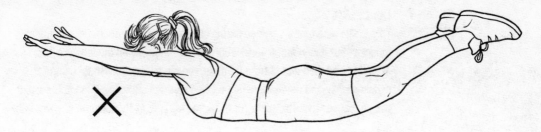

*Safe alternatives*

Mobility 4 **Prone back extension on forearms**

Mobility 5 **Prone back extension on hands**

EXERCISE **6**   **Opposite arm and leg raise**

This position again overloads the lumbar spine and the compression can cause damage to the vertebrae, discs and nerves.

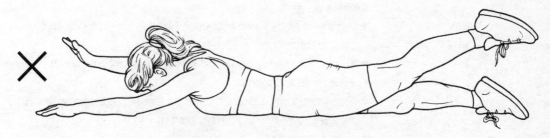

*Safe alternatives*

Mobility 1 **Back extension**

Mobility 4 **Prone back extension on forearms**

**EXERCISE 7**  **Double leg raise**

This is still a common exercise that is supposed to strengthen the abdominal muscles, but it is in fact a very dangerous exercise. When the legs are both extended and then raised from the floor, the hip flexors (iliopsoas) contract concentrically and the abdominal muscles contract statically. The lifted position usually causes hyperextension of the spine and the likely outcome is lower back pain.

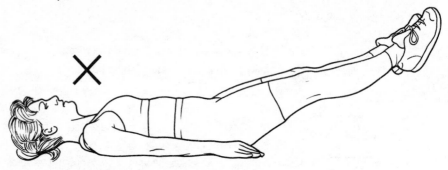

*Safe alternative*

**Bent leg sit-up**

- Begin lying on back with both knees bent, feet placed flat on the floor close to buttocks, hip width apart.
- Tilt the pelvis backwards so that the back is flat against the mat.
- Place hands on thighs.
- Slowly raise head and shoulders off the mat, sliding the hands towards the knees, then return to starting position.
- Repeat as required.

*Note  Slighty tilt the head towards the chest and hold while performing sit-ups.*

- Alternatively, place hands lightly on the side of the head to support the neck.

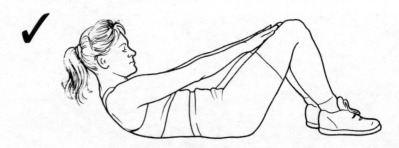

**EXERCISE 8**   **Straight leg toe touch**

Another common sporting warm-up exercise that is meant to increase the range of movement of the hamstrings. However, if you are very flexible and can easily touch the floor when leaning forward, this position will not stretch the hamstrings. If you are less flexible, this position will cause considerable strain on the lumbar spine as the muscles in the back cannot support the spine in this flexed position. The bouncing action which usually accompanies this exercise is counter-productive in terms of developing flexibility as the stretch reflex can occur, causing the muscles of the hamstrings to contract rather than lengthen.

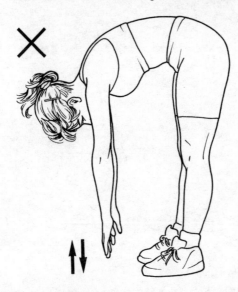

*Safe alternative*
Static stretching 41 **Sitting ham stretch**

EXERCISE **9**  **Hurdlers stretch**

This position of the bent leg in this stretch places excessive strain on the muscles in the inner thigh, while the outward rotation of the leg can strain the medial colateral ligament and the meniscus cartilage in the knee. The common result is knee joint instability and pain.

It might be argued that it is a functional requirement for hurdlers. However, hurdlers hit the hurdlers stretch position in the air. It is not necessary even for elite hurdlers to put themselves at risk and cause knee damage as there are many ways to stretch the necessary muscles effectively.

*Safe alternative*
Static stretching 40 **Sitting one-legged ham stretch**

EXERCISE **10**  **Sitting knee stretch**

This position should be avoided by everyone, especially children, even if it is comfortable to sit like this. The potential damage is twice that of the hurdlers stretch, but the reasons are the same. It causes an extreme stretch of the knee extensors (quadriceps) which may lead to inflammation of the patellar bursa (in the knee).

*Safe alternative*
Static stretching 55 **Standing quads**

EXERCISE **11**    **Lying knee stretch**

This exercise must be avoided at all times. It causes extreme strain in both knees, the quadriceps muscles and the lumbar spine.

*Safe alternative*
Static stretching 56 **Side quads**

EXERCISE **12**   **Deep knee stretch**

This exercise places unnecessary strain on the knees and should be avoided. There are a number of exercises where it is important to bend the legs only to 90 degrees and no further – for example, side lunges. In sports such as weight lifting and volleyball, it is necessary to move through a full movement range past 90 degrees and down to the floor in a squat position. In these cases it is important to increase strength by using multi-gym equipment to accommodate this movement and protect the knee joint as much as possible.

*Safe alternative*
    Mobility 17 **Turned out squats**

## MOBILITY EXERCISES FOR WARMING UP

Mobility exercises are designed to loosen the joints and contribute to gently raising the body temperature. Perform the exercises smoothly and slowly before moving on to static stretching.

MOBILITY **1**

### Back extension

- Begin standing upright with feet parallel and hip width apart.
- Place hands on the lower back with the thumbs just above the pelvic bone, fingers on spinal column.
- Keeping the hips and legs still, slowly lean the upper body backwards as far as comfortable and then slowly come back to the centre.
- Repeat 8 times.

*Note  Do not hold the extended back position.*

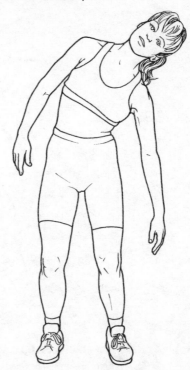

MOBILITY **2**

### Lateral leans

- Begin standing upright with feet parallel and hip width apart, arms down by sides.
- Bend knees, keeping feet flat on the floor and back upright. Ensure that the pelvis is centred.
- Lean directly to the right side and then the left side.
- Repeat 8 times.

**MOBILITY 3**  **Spinal rotations**

- Begin standing upright with feet either parallel and hip width apart, or rotated outwards as far as comfortable and placed shoulder width apart.
- Bend the knees, keeping the feet flat on the floor and back upright. Ensure that the pelvis is centred and the knees are directly over the toes.
- Keeping the pelvis and legs still, rotate the torso to the right side as far as comfortable and then rotate to the left side. The movement should be slow and controlled.
- Repeat 8 times.

**MOBILITY 4**  **Prone back extension on forearms** *(thoracic, lumbar spine)*

- Lie on floor on stomach, bending the arms and placing the forearms adjacent to the body.
- Pressing the forearms into the floor, slowly raise the upper spine from the floor and then slowly return to the floor.
- Repeat 4 times.

*Note  Do not hold the raised position.*

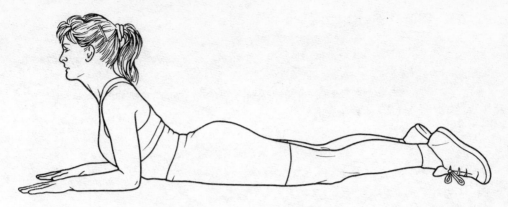

**MOBILITY 5**   **Prone back extension on hands** *(rectus abdominis, lumbar spine)*

- Lie on floor, face down.
- Place palms of hands on the floor underneath shoulders.
- Press down on the floor, raising torso but maintaining the hips in contact with the floor.
- Raise the torso only as far as comfortable. It is not necessary to straighten the arms.
- It is important to keep the head in alignment with the body for comfort. Do not take the head back.
- Rather than holding this stretch, move slowly into the stretch and slowly back down. Repeat 4 times.

MOBILITY **6**   **Neck rotation**

- Sit or stand upright.
- Keeping the body still, rotate the head slowly to the left side, as far round as possible.
- Repeat to the right side, keeping the chin level throughout the rotation.
- Repeat 4 times.

MOBILITY **7**   **Neck side flexion**

- Sit or stand upright.
- Lean head directly to the left side, keeping head facing front.
- Ensure shoulders remain down and still.
- Hold the stretch and relax, then repeat to the right side.
- Repeat 4 times.

MOBILITY **8**   **Forward neck flexion**

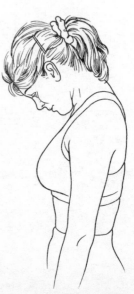

- Sit or stand upright.
- Slowly move the head directly forward, taking the chin towards the chest, and then slowly back to an upright position.
- Repeat 4 times.

MOBILITY **9**   **Shoulder shrugs**

- Begin standing upright with feet parallel and hip width apart, arms down by sides.
- Lift both shoulders up towards ears and then lower to starting position.
- Shoulder shrugs may be performed on right or left side or both together.
- Repeat 8 times.

MOBILITY **10**   **Shoulder rotations**

- Begin standing upright with feet parallel and hip width apart, arms down by sides.
- Rotate shoulders forwards, upwards and backwards.
- Repeat 8 times.

MOBILITY **11**   **Elbows flexion extension**

- Begin standing upright with feet parallel and hip width apart, arms down by sides.
- Place hands on shoulders (right hand on right shoulder, left hand on left shoulder), lifting arms so that the upper arms are in line with the shoulders and moved back as far as comfortable.
- Keeping the upper arms at shoulder height, move the arms forward so that the elbows touch in the centre and then back out to the sides again.
- Repeat 8 times.

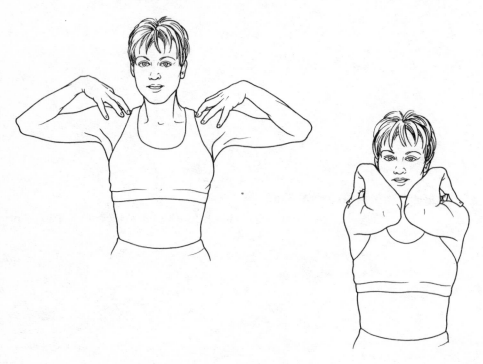

MOBILITY **12**   **Arm rotations**

- Begin standing upright with feet parallel and hip width apart, arms down by sides.
- Circle right arm forwards, upwards and then backwards, brushing the arm past the right side of the head and keeping the body still.
- This exercise may be performed with right arm, left arm or both arms, or alternate arms, rotating the arms in both directions.

    A popular athletics arm rotation is to simultaneously rotate the right and left arm in different directions.
- Repeat 8 times in each direction.

**MOBILITY 13**   **Arms overhead**

- Begin standing upright with feet parallel and hip width apart, arms down by sides.
- Bend knees, keeping feet flat and back straight. Ensure that the pelvis is centred.
- Reach overhead with the right arm, straightening the arm and leaning directly to the left side in order to feel a mild stretch on the right side. Then reach overhead with the left arm, leaning to the right side in order to stretch the left side.
- Repeat 8–16 times.

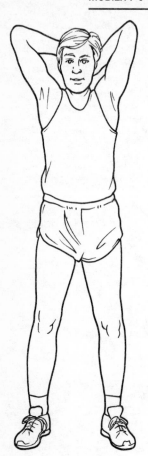

MOBILITY **14**    **Shoulder stretch**

- Begin standing upright with feet parallel and hip width apart, arms down by sides.
- With arms extended, cross arms in front of the body, placing the palms of the hands together.
- Raise the arms to shoulder height, then continue raising the arms overhead and as far back as comfortable. Now flex at the elbows, rotating the hands so that the fingers point downwards, pulling the shoulders out to the sides. Finally release the hands and slowly bring the arms back down by the sides.
- Perform this mobility exercise as a continuous sequence of movement.
- Repeat 4–8 times.

MOBILITY **15**    **Hip rotations**

- Begin standing upright with feet parallel and hip width apart, arms down by sides. Bend knees so that feet remain flat and the back is straight. Ensure that the pelvis is centred.
- Rotate hips clockwise and then anticlockwise.
- Repeat 4–8 times in each direction.

**MOBILITY 16**

### Parallel squats

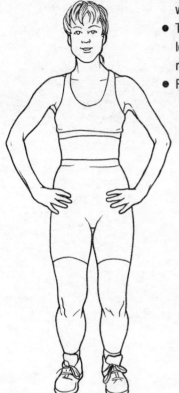

- Begin standing upright with feet parallel and hip width apart, arms down by sides.
- Bend knees and then straighten legs, ensuring that the knees are in alignment with the toes when the legs are bent.
- This exercise may be performed with flexion at the hips so that the athlete leans forward, keeping the back straight as the knees are bent, and then returns to an upright position when the legs are straight.
- Repeat 8–16 times.

**MOBILITY 17**

### Turned out squats

- Begin standing upright with the feet shoulder width apart or wider. The legs should be rotated outwards at the hip as far as comfortable.
- Place hands on hips and then bend the knees, ensuring that the knees are in alignment with the toes, and then return to standing position.
- In the bent squat position, ensure that the buttocks do not go below the level of the knees (90 degrees); it is not essential that all athletes squat down as far as this.
- Repeat 8–16 times.

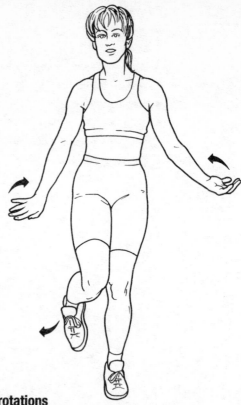

**MOBILITY 18    Ankle and wrist rotations**

- Begin standing upright with feet parallel and hip width apart, arms down by sides.
- Shift weight onto left foot, lifting the right foot just off the floor.
- Rotate the right ankle and both wrists in one direction and then the other.
- Rather than balancing on one leg to perform this exercise, you can hold onto a wall and circle one side of the body at a time.
- Repeat 8 times in both directions on the right and left sides.

## STATIC STRETCHING EXERCISES

Static stretching should be performed slowly, moving towards the end of the range of motion until mild tension is felt in the muscle. Stop at that point and relax. For guidelines on static stretching, see page 25.

## NECK

EXERCISE **1**

**Neck flexion** *(sternocleidomastoid, trapezius)*
- Place left hand on the upper right side of head.
- Slowly take the head towards the left shoulder.
- Hold the stretch and relax, then repeat to the right side.

## SHOULDERS

EXERCISE **2**

**Sitting shoulder stretch** *(anterior aspect of shoulders)*
- Sit upright on the floor with hands behind back, shoulder width apart, fingers pointing away from the body, palms flat on the floor.
- Now slide your bottom forward as far as possible, thereby increasing the stretch on the shoulders.
- Hold the stretch and relax.

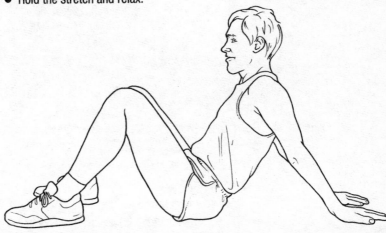

EXERCISE **3**   **Arm press** *(shoulder horizontal abduction/pectoralis)*

- Stand upright next to a wall.
- Place right arm behind body at shoulder height, along the wall.
- Ensure that the palm of the right hand is facing the wall.
- Now rotate torso away from the wall to stretch the chest muscles.
- Hold the stretch, relax, then repeat to the left side.

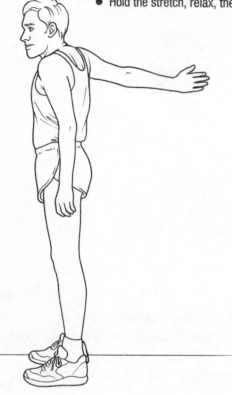

EXERCISE **4**   **Bent arm stretch** *(posterior aspect of shoulder, part of the long head of triceps)*

- Sit or stand upright with the right arm flexed at shoulder height, right hand towards left shoulder.
- Grasp your right arm just above the elbow with your left hand.
- Gently push the right arm back as far as comfortable, keeping the torso still.
- Hold the stretch and relax, then repeat on the left.

EXERCISE **5**    **Rear hand pulls** *(rotator cuff, supraspinatus)*
- Sit or stand upright with the left arm flexed behind the back.
- Grasp left wrist with right hand.
- Gently pull left arm sideways towards the right side across the midline of the back.
- Hold the stretch and relax, then repeat on the right arm.

EXERCISE **6**    **Prayer stretch** *(anterior aspect of shoulder, internal rotator cuff)*
- Stand or sit upright.
- Place your palms together behind your back, with fingers pointing upwards.
*Note  If palms together is not possible, touch fingertips instead.*
- Now draw your elbows backwards.
- Hold the stretch and relax.

**EXERCISE 7**    **Wall shoulder stretch** *(anterior aspect of shoulders)*

- Stand upright, placing hands behind back against a wall at about shoulder height, with the fingers pointing upwards.
- Slowly bend knees to lower the shoulders.
- Hold the stretch and relax.

**EXERCISE 8**    **Overhead stretch** *(axillary aspect of shoulders, shoulder flexors)*

- Stand or sit upright or lie flat on your back.
- Cross arms, placing palms together.
- Slowly raise your arms above head, with arms behind ears if possible.
- Hold the stretch and relax.

## ARMS

EXERCISE **9**    **Triceps stretch** *(triceps)*

- Stand or sit upright with the right arm and shoulder fully flexed and the elbow pointing towards the ceiling. The right hand should have the palm flat against the back.
- Grasp the raised elbow with the left hand.
- Gently pull the elbow behind the head.
- Hold the stretch and relax, then repeat on the left arm.

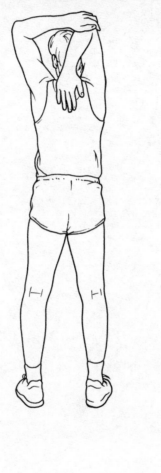

EXERCISE **10**    **Finger touch** *(triceps, rotator cuff, part of shoulder capsule)*

- Stand or sit upright with the right arm extended and raised above head, the left arm down by left side.
- Now flex both arms behind back, aiming to touch hands.
- Hold the stretch and relax, then repeat on the other side.

EXERCISE **11**    **Lats stretch** *(triceps, latissimus dorsi)*

- Stand or sit upright with the right arm and shoulder fully flexed, the elbow pointing towards the ceiling. The right hand should be flat against the back.
- Grasp the raised elbow with the left hand and gently pull the elbow behind the head.
- Slowly lean torso directly to the left side to feel the stretch on the right side of the back.
- Hold the stretch and relax, then repeat on the left side.

EXERCISE **12**    **Wrist reach** *(wrist extensors, brachio radialis)*

- Stand or sit upright, arms down by sides.
- Rotate hands so that palms face away from the body.
- Now reach fingers up towards the ceiling to feel the stretch in the wrist.
- Hold the stretch and relax.

EXERCISE **13**   **Wrist pulls** *(wrist extensors, brachio radialis)*

- Stand or sit upright, extending and raising the right arm in front of the body, palm facing downwards.
- Allow the hand to relax downwards and then grasp the hand with the left hand.
- Gently pull the right hand towards the inside of the forearm, as far as comfortable.
- Hold the stretch and relax, then repeat on the left hand.

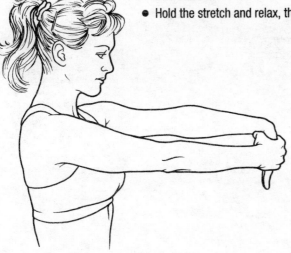

EXERCISE **14**   **Wrist flexors** *(forearm flexors)*

- Kneel on all fours, placing the hands directly below the shoulders, palms on the floor, fingers pointing towards the body.
- Slowly move the hips backwards as far as comfortable.
- Hold and relax.

EXERCISE **15**    **Assisted wrist flexors** *(forearm flexors)*

- Stand or sit upright, extending and raising the left arm in front of the body at shoulder height, palm facing upwards.
- Flex the left wrist and then grasp the hand with the right hand.
- Gently pull the left hand backwards as far as comfortable.
- Hold the stretch and relax, then repeat on the right arm.

EXERCISE **16**    **Rhomboids lift** *(rhomboids)*

- Stand or sit upright, flexing the left arm behind the back.
- Grasp wrist with right hand and lift arm away from body.
- Hold the stretch and relax, then repeat on the right arm.

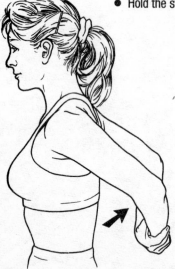

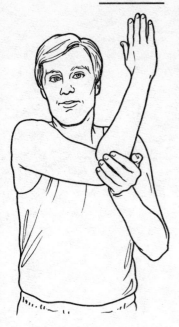

**EXERCISE 17**   **Angular rhomboids** *(rhomboids)*
- Stand or sit upright.
- Bend the right arm at right angles, with the forearm vertical and the elbow at shoulder height.
- Place the right arm across the midline of the body towards the left side.
- Place the left hand behind the right elbow and gently pull the right arm towards the left side to feel the stretch between the shoulder blades.
- Hold the stretch and relax, then repeat on the left side.

## UPPER BACK

**EXERCISE 18**   **Upper back hug** *(thoracic rib junctions)*
- Stand with feet parallel and hip width apart or sit upright.
- Cross and flex both arms, taking hands to opposite shoulders.
- If standing, bend knees.
- Now lean forward, curving upper back.
- Hold the stretch and relax.

*Caution  Do not hold breath.*

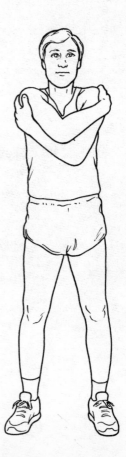

EXERCISE **19**  **Upper and lower back hug** *(cervical, thoracic and lumbar spine)*
- Stand with feet parallel and hip width apart or sit upright.
- Cross and flex both arms, taking hands to opposite shoulders.
- If standing, bend knees.
- Now lean forward, curving both the upper and lower back.
- Hold the stretch and relax

*Caution  Do not hold breath.*

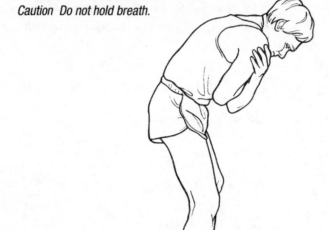

EXERCISE **20**  **Shoulder stretch** *(posterior aspect of shoulders)*
- Kneel on all fours, keeping hips either directly above knees or slightly towards heels.
- Slide the hands forward as far as possible with arms extended.
- Now gently lower the shoulders towards the floor.
- Hold the stretch and relax.

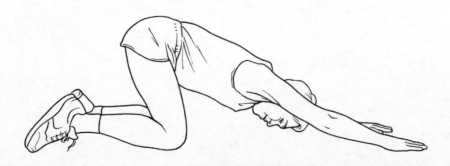

## LOWER BACK

EXERCISE **21**  **Sitting back stretch** (*lumbar spine*)
- Sit upright in a chair, arms down by sides.
- Slowly lean forward, relaxing torso on legs.
- Hold the stretch and relax.

EXERCISE **22**  **Lying back curl** (*lumbar spine*)
- Lie on back, bending both knees in towards chest.
- Place arms around legs, hugging knees to chest.
- Lift the lower back off the floor slightly.
- Hold the stretch and relax.

*Caution  If you have back problems, do not hold this stretch. Instead, move into the lifted-back position, then slowly return to starting position with head and lower back on the floor. Repeat slowly several times.*

EXERCISE **23**    **Standing back curl** *(thoracic and lumbar spine)*

- Begin standing upright with feet parallel and hip width apart.
- Bend knees and then lean forward from hips, curving the back. Place arms on back of lower leg.
- Hold the stretch and relax.

*Caution  Do not perform this stretch if you have back problems.*

*Note  Individuals with good flexibility in the hamstrings will be able to straighten legs whilst maintaining the back curl.*

EXERCISE **24**    **Pelvic tilt**

- Lie on back with both knees bent; feet should be parallel and placed hip width apart.
- Back should be flat on the floor.
- Slowly tilt the pelvis forwards to arch the lower back whilst keeping shoulders and buttocks on the floor.
- Now return lower back to the floor, pressing the back into the floor to tilt the pelvis slightly backwards.

*Note  This exercise is particularly helpful in providing some relief from back pain.*

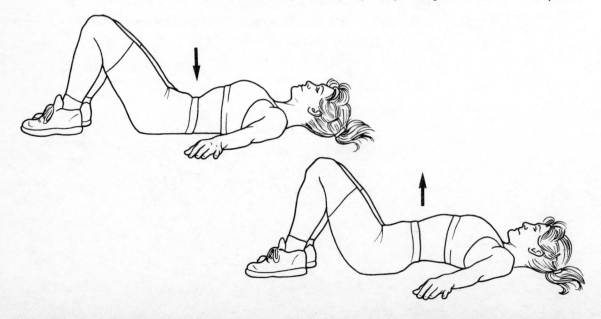

**EXERCISE 25**

**Sitting spinal twist** *(thoracic spine, internal/external obliques)*

- Sit on the floor with legs crossed and back upright.
- Rotate torso to the right side, placing right hand behind back on the floor.
- Place left hand just above right knee, using the hand as a lever to increase the spinal rotation.
- Hold the stretch and relax, then repeat to the left side.

*Note  This exercise may be performed sitting on a chair.*

**EXERCISE 26**

**One-armed side stretch** *(lateral torso)*

- Begin standing upright with feet turned out, shoulder width apart.
- Bend knees, keeping feet flat on the floor and back upright. The pelvis should be centred.
- Place the left hand on the outside of the left thigh, then extend right arm above head.
- Now lean torso and right arm directly to the left side as far as comfortable.
- Hold the stretch and relax, then repeat to the other side.

*Note  Remember to breathe in the stretch position! This stretch could be performed with both arms down by sides to make it easier.*

## CHEST

EXERCISE **27**   **Behind back chest stretch** *(pectoralis, anterior rotator cuff)*
- Stand or sit upright.
- Clasp hands behind back.
- Now raise arms as far back as comfortable, maintaining an upright posture.
- Hold the stretch and relax.

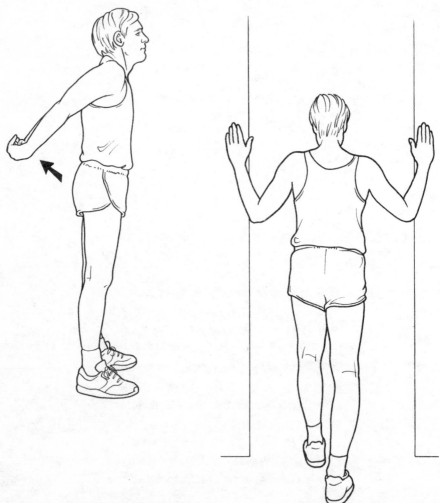

EXERCISE **28**   **'W' chest stretch** *(collarbone section of pectoralis muscle)*
- Stand facing an open doorway, with feet parallel and hip width apart.
- Place one foot in front of the other, bending the front leg to stabilize the body.
- Place the hands on the door surround at shoulder height.
- Now lean the torso forward to feel the stretch in the chest muscles.
- Hold the stretch and relax.

EXERCISE **29**   **Square chest stretch** *(breastbone section of pectoralis)*
- Stand facing an open doorway, with feet parallel and hip width apart.
- Place one foot in front of the other, bending the front leg to stabilize the body.
- Place the hands on the door surround so that the elbows are in line with the shoulders.
- Lean the torso forward to feel the stretch in the chest.
- Hold the stretch and relax.

*Caution  This exercise is not advisable for people with unstable shoulders.*

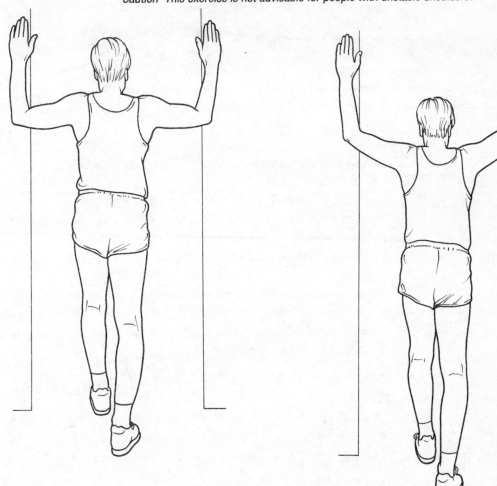

EXERCISE **30**   **'U' chest stretch** *(rib section of pectoralis bilaterally)*
- Stand facing an open doorway, with feet parallel and hip width apart.
- Place one foot in front of the other, bending the front leg to stabilize the body.
- Place the hands on the door surround so that the elbows are above the ears.
- Lean torso forward to feel the stretch in the chest muscles.
- Hold the stretch and relax.

## ABDOMEN

EXERCISE **31**   **Supine stomach stretch** *(rectus abdominis)*
- Lie on floor on back.
- Extend the arms above the head and stretch the body from the fingertips to the toes, emphasizing the stomach muscles.
- Hold the stretch and then relax.

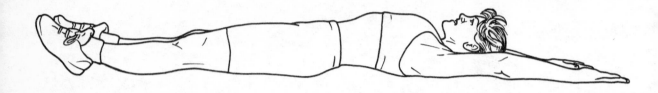

EXERCISE **32**   **Prone stomach stretch** *(rectus abdominis, lumbar spine)*
- Lie on floor face down.
- Place palms of hands on the floor underneath shoulders.
- Press down on the floor, raising torso but keeping the hips in contact with the floor.
- Raise the torso only as far as comfortable. It is not necessary to straighten the arms.
- It is important to keep the head in alignment with the body for comfort. Do not take the head back.
- Rather than holding this stretch, move slowly into the stretch and slowly back down. Repeat this several times.

## HIPS

EXERCISE **33**  **Knee hug** *(gluteals/upper hamstrings)*
- Lie on the floor on your back.
- Bring left knee up towards chest, holding on with both arms just below left knee.
- Ensure that the right leg remains straight throughout the stretch.
- Hold the stretch and relax, then repeat with the right leg.

EXERCISE **34**  **Kneeling hip stretch** *(hip flexors)*
- Begin kneeling on the floor, with the body upright.
- Place the right foot in front, so that the ankle is directly below the knee.
- Place the hands on the floor, fingers pointing forward, on either side of the right foot. For individuals who are very flexible, it will be more comfortable to place both hands to the left of the right foot.
- Now stretch the left leg back as far as comfortable with the knee on the floor. You should feel the stretch in the front of the hip.
- To increase this stretch, lower the left hip towards the floor.

## BUTTOCKS

EXERCISE **35**   **Crossed-leg gluteals** *(gluteals)*

- Sit on the floor with legs crossed and body upright.
- Lean forward from the base of the spine, keeping back straight, and place the hands on the floor in front of the body.
- Hold the stretch and relax.

*Note  If a tight back restricts movement forward, it will be more comfortable to place the hands behind the back on the floor. From this position you can use the arms to help you to lean forward.*

EXERCISE **36**   **Supine gluteals stretch** *(gluteus maximus, upper hamstrings)*

- Lie on floor on back with both knees bent, feet on the floor hip width apart, and pelvis tilted slightly backwards so that the lower back is completely flat on the floor. Place arms on the floor, down by sides.
- Turning the left leg outwards, place the left foot just above the right knee.
- Now lift the right foot off the ground, towards the chest as far as comfortable to feel the stretch in the left buttock.
- Hold the stretch and relax, then repeat on the right side.

*Caution  Ensure that the back remains flat during this stretch.*

*Note  To increase this stretch, place arms around the upper left leg, gently pulling the leg towards the chest.*

**EXERCISE 37** **Supine spinal rotation** *(lumbothoracic spine, gluteus maximus)*

- Lie on floor on back with both legs extended, arms by sides.
- Bend the right leg, bringing the knee towards the chest as far as comfortable. Keep the left leg extended.
- Extend the right arm directly out to the right side, palm facing down.
- Place the left hand just below the right knee, and gently rotate the right leg towards the left side, only moving as far as comfortable whilst keeping both shoulders in contact with the floor.
- Hold the stretch and relax, then repeat on the left side.

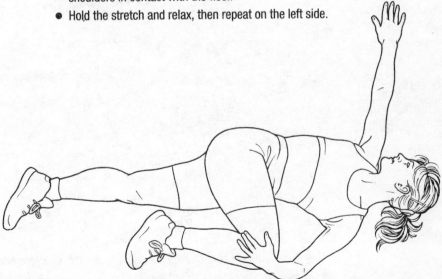

EXERCISE **38**

**Sitting spinal hip rotation** (*gluteus maximus, spinal rotators*)
**Step 1**

- Sit on the floor with back as straight as possible.
- Place hands behind back on floor to support the upright spinal position.
- Bend left leg, crossing left foot to the outside of the right leg.

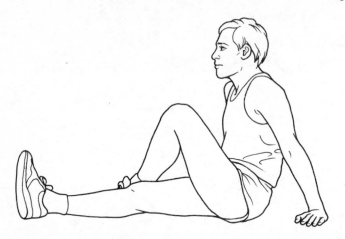

**Step 2**

- Now bend the right leg, taking the right foot towards the left hip.

*Note If this position is uncomfortable, go back to Step 1 and then add the spinal twist in Step 3.*

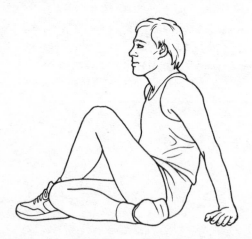

**Step 3**

- Keeping the body as upright as possible, rotate the torso towards the left side. The left hand remains on the floor behind the back for support.
- Bend the right arm, placing the elbow on the outside of the left knee, with the forearm along the outer left thigh.

- Rotate head towards the left side as far as is comfortable.
- Twist torso until mild tension is felt on the bent thigh, buttocks and back. Stop, relax and hold this position. Repeat to the other side.

*Note  To increase this stretch, use right arm as a lever, pushing against left leg to increase rotation.*

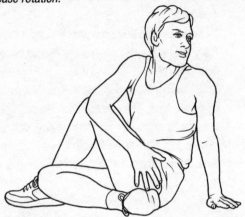

EXERCISE **39**   **Advanced crossed gluteal stretch** *(gluteals)*

- Sit on the floor with back upright and legs extended out in front of the body.
- Bend the left leg over the right, placing left foot beside right knee.
- Now, bend right leg, taking the right foot towards the left hip.
- Lean the torso forward as far as is comfortable, placing the hands on the floor in front of the body.
- Hold the stretch and relax, then repeat to the other side.

## UPPER LEGS

EXERCISE **40**

**Sitting one-legged ham stretch** *(hamstrings, lumbar spine)*
- Sit on the floor with back upright, with the right leg extended out in front and the left leg flexed and turned out so that the left foot is placed adjacent to the right knee.
- The right leg should remain straight, with the foot vertical, but relaxed.
- Place the hands either in front or behind the body, whichever is the most comfortable.
- Now keeping the back straight, lean forward from the base of the spine as far as comfortable. The head should also be kept in alignment with the back.
- Hold the stretch and relax, then repeat with the left leg.

*Note  If you find it difficult to lean forward, place hands behind back during stretch. If the calf muscle in the extended leg is very tense, flex the knee slightly.*

EXERCISE **41**

**Sitting ham stretch** *(hamstrings)*
- Sit on the floor with back upright, extending both legs out in front of the body.
- Place the hands either in front or behind the body, whichever is the most comfortable.
- Keeping the back straight and the head aligned with the back, lean forward from the base of the spine until mild tension is felt in the muscles on the back of the upper legs.
- Stop, hold the stretch and relax.

*Note  Flex the knees if the calf muscles hinder movement of the torso forward.*

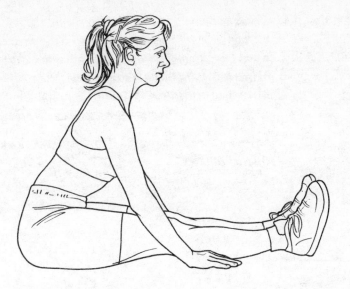

**EXERCISE 42**   **Supine one-legged ham stretch** *(hamstrings)*

- Lie on your back on the floor with both legs bent, feet hip width apart and arms by sides.
- Slowly bring the right knee towards the chest as far as comfortable.
- Placing both hands on the lower leg, slowly extend the lower limb, taking the toes towards the head. The stretch will be felt in the muscles on the back of the upper leg.
- Hold the stretch, relax and then repeat on the left leg.

*Note  This hamstring stretch is strongly recommended in preference to all other hamstring stretches. This position isolates the hamstrings and offers a safe and effective stretch.*

**EXERCISE 43**  **Standing ham stretch** *(hamstrings/lumbar spine)*

- Stand upright with feet hip width apart and arms by sides.
- Bend knees, keeping back upright, then slowly lean the torso forward, taking the hands to the floor just in front of the feet.
- Hold the stretch and relax. DO NOT BOUNCE.

*Caution  If you have back problems, avoid this stretch.*

*Note  Very flexible individuals will be able to straighten legs in this position but DO NOT BOUNCE!*

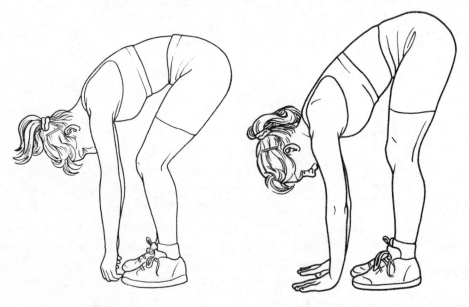

**EXERCISE 44**  **Crossed ham stretch** *(hamstrings)*

- Stand upright, then cross right leg over left, arms by sides.
- Slowly lean the torso forward, taking the hands towards the floor.
- Hold the stretch and relax. DO NOT BOUNCE.
- Slowly return to the starting position, then repeat this on the left leg.

*Caution  If you have back problems, avoid this stretch.*

**EXERCISE 45**   **Feet apart ham stretch** *(hamstrings)*

- Stand upright with feet parallel and hip width apart.
- Place the right heel directly forward, then place the right foot flat.
- Bend left knee, keeping the right leg straight.
- Now lean the torso forward as far as is comfortable on the hamstrings, placing the hands on the bent leg.
- Hold the stretch and relax, then repeat on the left leg.

*Caution  Ensure that the hips are kept in alignment as the body leans forwards and downwards. DO NOT TILT HIPS!*

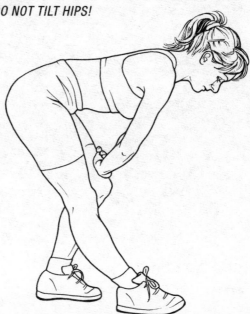

**EXERCISE 46**  **Standing ham and calf stretch** *(hamstrings and gastrocnemius)*

- Stand upright with feet parallel, hip width apart.
- Place the right heel directly in front, straightening the leg. This time the heel remains in position with the toes pointing up.
- Bend left knee, keeping the right leg straight.
- Now lean the torso forward as far as is comfortable on the hamstrings and calf, placing the hands lightly on the bent leg.
- Hold the stretch and relax, then repeat on the left leg.

**EXERCISE 47**

**Raised-leg ham stretch** *(upper hamstrings, lumbar spine)*

- Stand upright with body straight.
- Slowly raise extended right leg directly in front of body and place the foot on a stable bar or chair for support.
- Ensure that the height of the object is appropriate to your flexibility. Do not over-stretch.
- Maintain a straight back and lean forward towards right leg. DO NOT CURL SPINE.
- Hold the stretch and relax, then repeat on the left leg.

*Caution  This stretch is not recommended for people who suffer from back problems.*

*Note  This is a useful stretch for outdoor sports where it is not possible to sit or lie down to stretch the hamstrings.*

## INNER THIGH

EXERCISE **48**   **Inner thigh lunge** *(adductors)*
- Stand upright with feet about shoulder width apart.
- Turn right foot outwards to a comfortable position.
- Lunge onto the right leg so that the knee is directly above the ankle.
- With the left foot pointing forwards, extend the left leg as far to the left side as comfortable.
- Hold the stretch and relax, then repeat lunging on the left leg.

EXERCISE **49**   **Sitting inner thigh stretch** *(adductors)*
- Sit on the floor with back upright.
- Turn legs out from the hips, bend knees and bring soles of the feet together towards buttocks.
- Place hands just below ankles.
- Lean torso forward from the hips, keeping the back straight and the head in alignment.
- Hold the stretch and relax.

*Note  To increase the stretch, bring the heels further towards the buttocks.*

EXERCISE **50**    **Sitting elbows on knees stretch** *(adductors)*

- Sit on the floor with back upright.
- Turn legs out from the hips, bend knees and bring soles of the feet together towards buttocks.
- Place hands just above the ankles, elbows on the knees.
- Gently press legs down towards the floor.
- Hold the stretch and relax.

EXERCISE **51**    **Supine inner thigh** *(adductors)*

- Lie flat on back with body straight.
- Turn legs out from the hips, bend knees and bring soles of the feet together towards buttocks.
- Hold the stretch and relax.

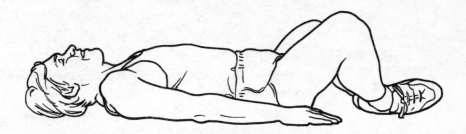

**EXERCISE 52**

### Sitting straddle *(adductors)*

- Sit upright on the floor with both legs extended in a comfortable straddle position.
- Lean forward from the base of the spine, keeping the back as straight as possible.
- Place the hands on floor either between legs or behind hips, depending on which is most comfortable.
- Hold the stretch and relax.

*Note  If this stretch is uncomfortable around the knee joint, slightly bend the knee.*

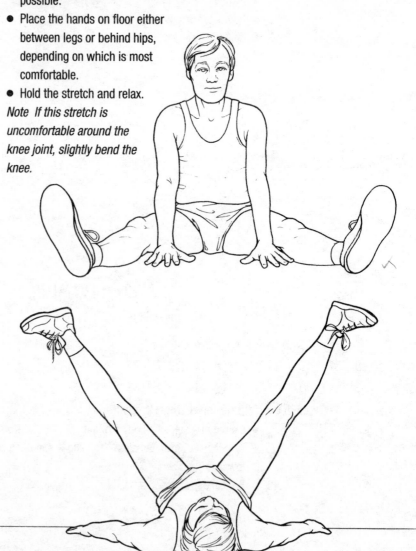

**EXERCISE 53**

### Wall straddle *(adductors)*

- Lie on the floor perpendicular to a wall, placing the buttocks and extended legs against the wall.
- Ensure that the lower back is flat and pressed against the floor.
- Straddle the legs as far as comfortable.
- Hold the stretch and relax.

## OUTER THIGH

EXERCISE **54**

**Outer hip stretch** *(gluteals, iliotibial tract)*

- Stand upright facing a stable object that you can hold onto for support, such as a rail, chair or table.
- Place right leg behind left and slide it to the left side as far as comfortable.
- Ensure that the torso remains upright.
- Hold the stretch and relax, then repeat on the left leg.

## FRONT OF THIGH

**Standing quads** *(quadriceps)*

- Stand upright with feet hip width apart and parallel.
- Place left hand on a wall for balance.
- Bend the right leg, grasping the ankle with the right hand.
- Pull the right heel towards the buttocks, keeping the right thigh in alignment with the left.
- Hold the stretch and relax.

*Caution  Allow the right foot to naturally gravitate toward the midline of the body.*
*DO NOT PULL THE RIGHT FOOT TO THE OUTSIDE OF THE LEG AND PUT THE KNEE OUT OF ALIGNMENT.*

EXERCISE **56**   **Side quads** *(quadriceps)*

- Lie on left side with legs extended, resting along an extended left arm or supporting head with left hand.
- Bend the left leg at 90 degrees at the knee to make the position more stable.
- Now bend the right leg, grasping the right ankle with the right hand and pulling the foot towards the buttocks.
- Ensure that both thighs remain in alignment.
- Hold the stretch and relax, then repeat on the left leg.

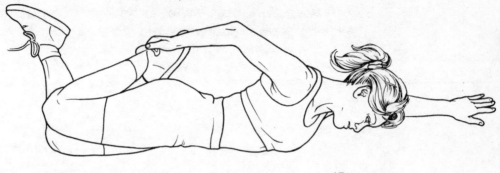

*(From above)*

EXERCISE **57**   **Prone quads** *(quadriceps)*

- Lie on the floor face down with legs extended.
- Bend right leg, grasping ankle with the left hand. This will allow the knee to be in a natural position. If it is impossible to perform this stretch with opposite hand to foot because of limb length or flexibility, use left hand to left foot and right hand to right foot.
- Bend the free arm and rest head on hand, with the head in alignment face down.
- Hold the stretch and relax, then repeat on the left leg.
- If the foot of the bent leg can comfortably touch the buttocks, lift the thigh off the floor, keeping the hips pressed against the floor to increase the stretch.

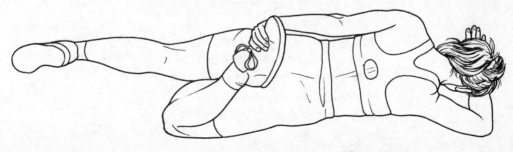

*(From above)*

## LOWER LEGS

EXERCISE **58** **Wall calf stretch** *(gastrocnemius)*

- Stand upright with feet parallel, hip width apart. This stretch may be performed against a wall or freestanding.
- Place hands at shoulder height against a wall. If freestanding, arms should remain relaxed by sides.
- Lunge forward on right leg, with the knee directly above the ankle. Stretch the left leg back as far as comfortable with the foot down flat.
- The body should be in alignment, with a straight line from head to left foot.
- Hold the stretch and relax, then repeat the lunge on the left leg.
- To increase the stretch, move the hips forward towards the wall, or press the heel of the back foot towards the floor.

EXERCISE **59** **Step calf stretch** *(gastrocnemius)*

- This stretch is designed to be performed on a step.
- Stand upright on a step, with feet parallel and hip width apart, holding onto a handrail if possible.
- Move the right foot back so that the instep is level with the edge of the step.
- Now keep the body weight forward while pressing the heel downwards.
- Hold the stretch and relax, then repeat on the left leg.

EXERCISE **60**

**Toes in calf stretch** *(gastrocnemius)*

- Place hands on a wall at shoulder height.
- Stand with feet hip width apart and pointing inwards, then roll onto the outsides of the feet.
- Lean the body forward whilst keeping the body in alignment in order to feel the stretch on both calf muscles.

*Note  This is a very good exercise to counter any tendency for the foot to roll outwards.*

EXERCISE **61**  **One-legged calf stretch** *(gastrocnemius)*

- Lie on back with left leg bent, foot placed on the floor.
- Raise the right leg towards head as far as comfortable.
- Slowly flex the right foot to stretch the gastrocnemius.
- Hold the stretch and relax, then repeat on the left foot.

EXERCISE **62**  **Flexed-foot calf stretch** *(gastrocnemius)*

- Stand upright facing a wall with feet parallel and hip width apart.
- Flex the right foot, placing the ball of the foot against the wall.
- Place hands against the wall at shoulder height.
- Lean body towards wall to stretch the right calf muscle.
- Hold the stretch and relax, then repeat on the left leg.

EXERCISE **63**   **Wall Achilles stretch** *(soleus, Achilles)*

- Stand upright with feet parallel, hip width apart. This stretch may be performed against a wall or freestanding.
- Place hands at shoulder height against a wall. If freestanding, arms should remain relaxed by sides.
- Lunge forward on right leg, with the knee directly above ankle. Stretch the left leg back as far as comfortable with the foot flat on the floor.
- Slowly flex the left leg to stretch the lower calf.
- Hold the stretch and relax, then repeat on the right leg.

**EXERCISE 64**   **Bar stool stretch** *(soleus, Achilles)*

- Stand upright with feet parallel, hip width apart.
- Place the left leg directly forward so that the left heel is in line with the right toes.
- Maintain good posture and bend both knees to feel the stretch on the lower calf of the back leg.
- Hold the stretch and relax, then repeat on the left leg.

*Caution  Ensure that both feet are kept flat on the floor during the stretch.*

**EXERCISE 65**   **Kneeling Achilles stretch** *(soleus, Achilles)*

- Begin by kneeling, then place the right foot on the floor in line with the left knee.
- Place the hands on the floor in front and to the left of the right foot.
- Now lean the body forward, to stretch the soleus of the right foot.
- Hold the stretch and relax, then repeat on the left leg.

EXERCISE **66**  **Lower leg stretch** *(tibialis posterior)*
- Sit on the floor with back upright and right leg extended in front of the body. The left leg is flexed and turned out at the hip, so that the left foot is placed on the floor just above the right knee.
- The right foot should begin vertical but relaxed.
- Lean the torso forward and grasp the right foot with the right hand.
- Rotate the foot inwards to stretch the lateral lower leg.
- Hold the stretch and relax, then repeat on the left leg.

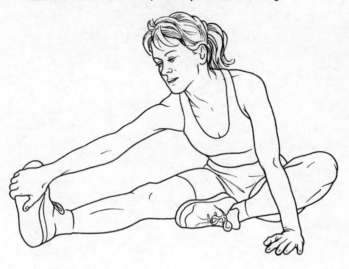

EXERCISE **67**  **Toe crush** *(ankle extension)*
- Stand upright with feet parallel, hip width apart.
- Shift weight to left foot and lift right heel, placing the front of the toes on the floor.
- Slowly shift some weight to the right foot, pressing gently downwards.
- Hold the stretch and relax, then repeat on the left foot.

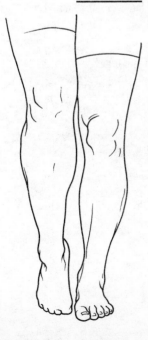

**EXERCISE 68**    **Kneeling ankle stretch** *(plantar flexion, tibialis anterior)*

- Begin by kneeling with body upright and only flexed at the knees.
- Slowly lower buttocks towards heels, using hands on floor for support.
- Lower buttocks onto heels if possible. If not, lower as far as comfortable.
- Hold the stretch and relax.

*Note  To take this stretch further, place a rolled towel under the mid foot.*

**EXERCISE 69**    **Ankle stretcher** *(plantar flexion)*

- Begin by sitting on a chair on the floor, crossing right leg over left so that the right foot can be manipulated.
- Extend the right foot, stretching the toes.
- Place right hand on the heel and grasp the top of foot underhand with the left.
- Use hands to increase the extension of toes, feeling the stretch on the front of the foot.

## TOES

**EXERCISE 70**

**Toes towards shin** *(flexion of toes)*
- Begin by sitting on a chair or on the floor, crossing right leg over left so that the right foot can be manipulated.
- Place one hand on the right ankle and one hand on the underside of the toes and ball of foot.
- Gently pull toes towards shin.
- Hold the stretch and relax, then repeat on the left foot.

**EXERCISE 71**

**Foot press** *(flexion of toes)*
- Stand upright, with feet parallel, hip width apart.
- Shift weight to left foot, then raise the right heel so that only the ball of the foot is in contact with the floor.
- Gently shift some weight to the right foot, pressing the ball of the foot into the floor.
- Hold the stretch and relax, then repeat on the left foot.

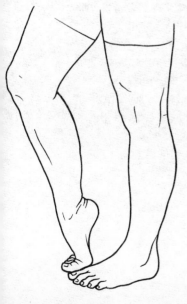

## PNF PARTNER STRETCHES

There are two PNF techniques recommended for athletes. These are hold–relax (HR) and contract–relax–agonist–contract (CRAC). Guidelines for maintenance and development of flexibility using PNF are on page 26.

**Stretching should not be painful. If you experience pain during PNF stretches, stop, then decrease the stretch on the muscle or use less force during contractions. If pain continues, stop PNF until the cause of pain is known.**

**Hold–relax** begins with the partner slowly moving the muscle or body part of the stretches towards the end of range of motion, stopping and holding at the onset of tension in the lengthened muscle. The stretcher then begins to perform a 6-second isometric (static) contraction of the lengthened target muscle whilst the partner resists and maintains the stretcher's body part in a static position. The intensity of the contraction should begin low and slowly build up to 100 per cent effort, breathing throughout. This is followed by 6 seconds of relaxation in the same position. Then the partner, in consultation with the stretcher, slowly moves the body part to increase the stretch. The process is repeated up to four times, as appropriate.

**Contract–relax–agonist–contract** begins in a similar manner to hold–relax. The partner slowly moves the lengthened muscle or body part towards the end of range of motion, stopping and holding at the onset of tension in the lengthened muscle. The stretcher then begins to perform a 6-second isometric (static) contraction of the lengthened target muscle whilst the partner resists and maintains the stretcher's body part in a static position. The intensity of the contraction should begin low and slowly build to 100 per cent effort, breathing throughout. This is followed by 6 seconds of relaxation in the same position. At this point CRAC departs from the HR procedure.

Immediately following relaxation the stretcher performs a concentric (shortening) contraction of the opposing muscles, again for 6 seconds. The partner offers resistance but allows the body part to move, thereby increasing the range of motion. The stretcher then relaxes for another 6 seconds. The process is repeated from the beginning up to four times, as appropriate.

The following PNF stretches are described using the HR technique but are applicable for CRAC techniques too, using the above procedure.

PNF **1**  **Shoulders** *(anterior aspect of shoulders, anterior deltoids)*

- The person to be stretched (the stretcher) begins by kneeling with body upright on the floor, or sitting on a chair with the back upright. If the stretcher is shorter than the partner, this stretch may be performed standing.
- The stretcher intertwines fingers and places hands behind head, moving the elbows out to the sides.
- The partner is positioned behind the stretcher and places hands on the stretcher's elbows.
- The stretcher tries to move elbows forward, performing a 6-second isometric contraction of the anterior deltoids, whilst the partner maintains the stretcher's arms in a static contraction. The intensity of the contraction should begin low and slowly build to 100 per cent effort, breathing throughout.
- The stretcher relaxes for 6 seconds, then the partner (in consultation with the stretcher) slowly attempts to increase the stretch by moving the elbows further out to the side, stopping at the onset of tension.
- Repeat this sequence of stretching up to 4 times, reducing repetitions when near maximum flexibility is achieved.

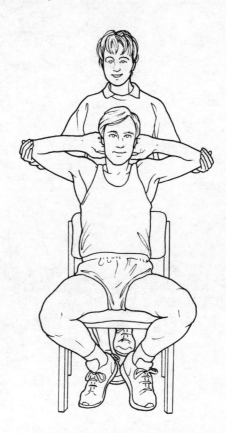

**PNF 2** **Triceps** *(triceps)*

- The stretcher begins by either sitting on a chair or kneeling on the floor. The right shoulder and elbow are fully flexed so that the elbow points to the ceiling and the palm of the right hand touches the back.
- The partner stands facing the right side of the stretcher, with one hand stabilizing the back part of the shoulder and the other cupped around the stretcher's right elbow.
- The stretcher isometrically contracts the triceps and tries to move elbow towards right side of torso for 6 seconds whilst the partner maintains the arm in a static position.
- The stretcher relaxes for 6 seconds in this position. Then the partner (in consultation with the stretcher) attempts to increase the stretch by moving the elbow further towards the head until the onset of tension.
- Repeat this sequence of stretching up to 4 times, reducing repetitions when near maximum flexibility is achieved.

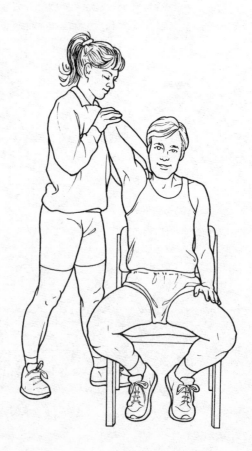

PNF **3** **Wrist flexors** *(flexor carpi radialis, flexor carpi ulnaris, palmaris longus)*
Raquet players will particularly benefit from PNF stretches for the wrist and
forearm muscles.

- The stretcher begins by lying on the floor, face up. This stretch may be
  performed either sitting or standing, as long as the target arm remains
  immobilized.
- The stretcher's right arm is bent at 90 degrees and the hand flexed as far as
  possible so that the palm faces the ceiling.
- The partner places one hand on the right wrist of the stretcher to stabilize the
  arm. The other hand is matched, palm down, against the flexed hand.
- The stretcher performs an isometric (static) contraction of the wrist flexors for
  6 seconds by attempting to push forward against the resistance of the partner's
  hand.
- The stretcher relaxes for 6 seconds in this position. The partner (in consultation
  with the stretcher) then attempts to increase the stretch, gently flexing the
  hand back further by pushing on the stretcher's fingers.
- Repeat this sequence of stretching up to 4 times, reducing repetitions when
  near maximum flexibility is achieved.

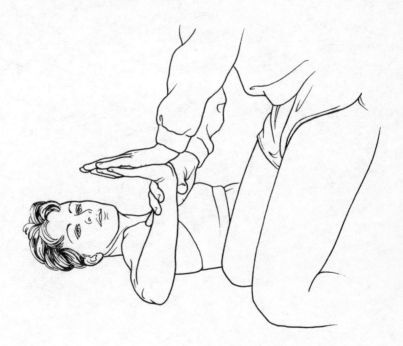

PNF **4**   **Wrist extensors** (extensor carpi radialis longus, extensor carpi radialis brevis, extensor carpi ulnaris)

- The stretcher begins by lying on the floor, face up. This stretch may also be performed either sitting or standing, as long as the target arm remains immobilized.
- The stretcher's right arm is bent at 90 degrees and the hand is bent forward as far as possible with the fingers curled in a relaxed fist.
- The partner places one hand on the right wrist of the stretcher to stabilize the arm and the other over the stretcher's fist.
- The stretcher performs an isometric contraction for 6 seconds, attempting to raise the hand backwards against the resistance of the partner's hand.
- The stretcher relaxes for 6 seconds in this position. Then the partner (in consultation with the stretcher) attempts to increase the stretch by gently bending the wrist forward to the onset of tension.
- Repeat this sequence of stretching up to 4 times, reducing repetitions when near maximum flexibility is achieved.

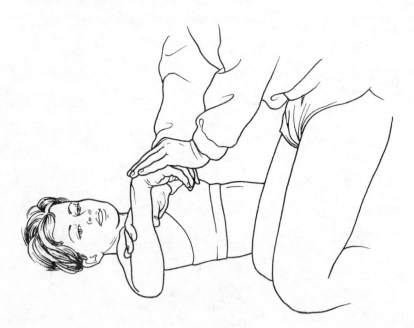

**PNF 5**  **Prone chest and shoulders** *(pectoralis and anterior aspect of shoulders)*

- The stretcher begins by lying face down on the floor with legs extended. Arms are abducted and extended to the sides at 90 degrees, with the palms of the hands facing down.

- The partner stands astride the stretcher with feet turned out as far as comfortable. The partner bends at the knee and squats, keeping the back straight. Now the partner leans forward from the hips and grasps the wrists of the stretcher, lifting the arms upwards and extending the arms back as far as comfortable. The arms of the stretcher should be completely relaxed and passive during this first stage.

- The stretcher performs an isometric contraction for 6 seconds by attempting to take the arms towards the floor whilst the partner offers resistance against any movement.

- The stretcher relaxes for 6 seconds in this position. Then the partner attempts to increase the stretch by pushing the stretcher's arms further back towards each other until the onset of tension.

- Repeat this sequence of stretching up to 4 times, reducing repetitions when near maximum flexibility is achieved.

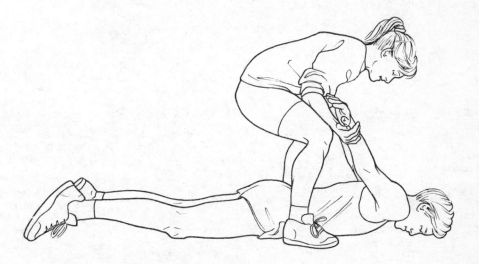

PNF **6** **Sitting chest** (*pectoralis, anterior deltoids*)

- This stretch is most easily performed with the stretcher sitting on a chair, although it could be performed kneeling on the floor.
- The stretcher sits upright with back pressed against the chair. The arms are bent at 90 degrees at the elbow and abducted so that the upper arms are in line with the shoulders.
- The partner stands behind the stretcher and cups hands around the stretcher's elbows.
- The stretcher performs an isometric contraction on the target muscles for 6 seconds, attempting to take the arms forward towards the mid-line of the body. The partner resists the contraction and maintains the stretcher's arms in a static position.
- The stretcher relaxes for 6 seconds. Then the partner (in consultation with the stretcher) increases the stretch on the pectoralis until tension occurs.
- Repeat this sequence of stretching up to 4 times, reducing repetitions when near maximum flexibility is achieved.

*Note  This PNF stretch may also be performed with the stretcher's arms in either a 'V' shape or 'W' shape in order to stretch different parts of the pectoralis.*

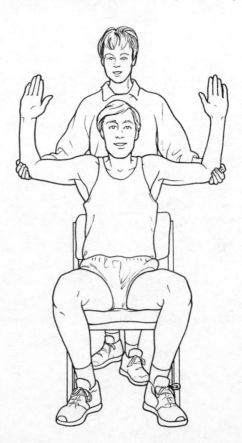

## PNF 7 Back extensors *(iliocostalis, longissimus, spinali)*

- The stretcher begins by sitting on the floor with both legs extended out in front. The knees are slightly bent, although individuals who have very good hamstring flexibility can keep the legs straight. The stretcher then leans forward as far as is comfortable, using the rectus abdominus and psoas to lengthen the back extensors to their current ROM. Stop and hold the position.

- The partner kneels behind the stretcher and places hands at either side of the vertical columns of the spine. If the stretcher can lean forward easily it is best to place the hands about the middle of the spine, but if the stretcher finds it difficult to lean forward it is best to place the hands higher up the back in order to be in a good position to resist the isometric contraction.

- The stretcher performs an isometric contraction of the back extensors for 6 seconds, attempting to push backwards against the hands of the partner. Do not use arms to push back.

- The stretcher relaxes for 6 seconds. Then the partner gently pushes the stretcher to lean further forward in order to increase the stretch of the back extensors.

- Repeat this sequence of stretching up to 4 times, reducing repetitions when near satisfactory flexibility is achieved.

*Note  This PNF stretch may also be performed cross-legged, with soles of feet together or with legs astride.*

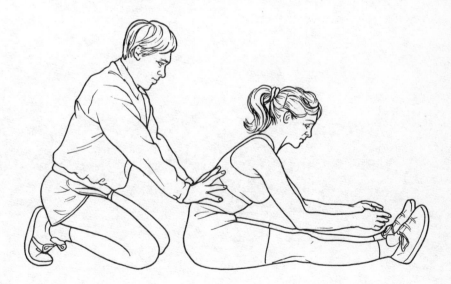

## PNF 8   Lying lower back *(psoas)*

- The stretcher lies on a table with the top of the legs at the edge of the table. The left leg is bent and the knee is moved towards the chest, thereby protecting the lower back, which is pressed flat against the table.
- The stretcher presses the right heel towards the floor to lengthen the right psoas to the current end of ROM.
- The partner stands facing the stretcher, allowing the left foot of the stretcher to rest against the partner whilst the other hand is placed just above the right knee of the stretcher.
- The stretcher performs an isometric contraction of the psoas for 6 seconds by attempting to lift the right knee towards the right shoulder. At the same time the partner resists the movement by applying equal and opposite force downwards using the left hand.
- The stretcher relaxes for 6 seconds in this position. Then the partner assists the stretcher to press the right heel towards the floor, thereby increasing the stretch on the psoas.

*Note  The partner should apply gentle pressure and not push to increase the stretch.*

- Repeat this sequence of stretching up to 4 times, reducing repetitions as the required range of movement is achieved.

- When stretching on the right side is completed, the partner should aid the stretcher to bend the right leg and place it on the partner's torso and then lower the left leg down in order to stretch the left psoas. When both sides are finished, the partner should help the stretcher to bring both knees towards chest, then the stretcher should push back using feet against partner in order to be able to sit up.

### PNF 9   Knee to shoulder *(piriformis)*

- The stretcher begins by lying face up on the floor with the left leg extended and the right knee flexed so that the knee moves towards the left shoulder as far as possible. This position lengthens the piriformis to the current end of ROM.
- The partner places both hands on the outside of the stretcher's right knee.
- The stretcher performs an isometric contraction of the piriformis for 6 seconds by attempting to push the right knee diagonally towards the partner. At the same time the partner resists the movement by applying equal and opposite force, retaining the stretcher's leg in a static position.
- The stretcher relaxes for 6 seconds in this position. Then the partner (in consultation with the stretcher) increases the stretch on the piriformis by gently pushing the knee towards the left shoulder.
- Repeat this sequence of stretching up to 4 times, reducing repetitions when the required ROM is achieved.

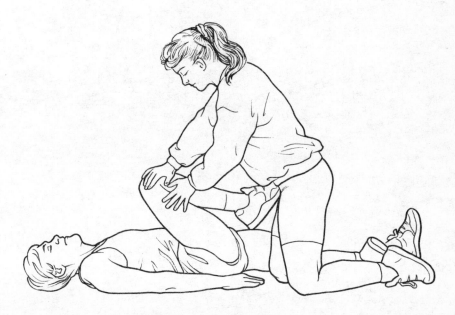

PNF **10**  **Bent leg hams** *(hamstrings)*

- The stretcher begins by lying face up, with the right leg flexed at the knee and lifted towards the head as far as comfortable. This position lengthens the hamstrings to the current end of ROM.
- The partner places the stretcher's right foot on their shoulder and places their right hand on the stretcher's left thigh to retain the leg on the floor, then places the left hand just above the stretcher's right knee.
- The stretcher performs an isometric contraction of the hamstrings for 6 seconds by attempting to push the leg downwards towards the floor. At the same time the partner resists the movement by applying equal and opposite force upwards.
- The stretcher relaxes for 6 seconds in this position. Then the partner straightens the stretcher's knee until tension occurs in the stretched muscle. This increases the stretch on the hamstrings.
- Repeat this sequence of stretching from this new position up to 4 times, reducing repetitions when the required ROM is achieved.

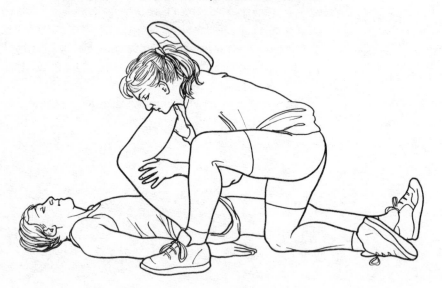

PNF **11**    **Supine straight leg hams** *(hamstrings)*

- The stretcher begins by lying face up on the floor. The right leg is lifted towards the head as far as comfortable. This position lengthens the hamstrings to the current end of ROM.
- The partner holds the stretcher's right foot and leg, placing the left hand just below the right knee and the right hand beneath the right heel. Ensure that the hips remain down on the floor during the contraction.
- The stretcher performs an isometric contraction of the hamstrings for 6 seconds by pushing the right leg downwards towards the floor. At the same time, the partner resists the movement by applying equal and opposite force in order to hold the leg in a static position.
- The stretcher relaxes for 6 seconds in this position. Then the partner attempts to move the right leg further towards the head, thereby increasing the stretch on the hamstrings.
- Repeat this sequence of stretching from this new position up to 4 times, reducing repetitions when the required ROM is achieved.

*Note  Less flexible people should bend the left leg for comfort.*

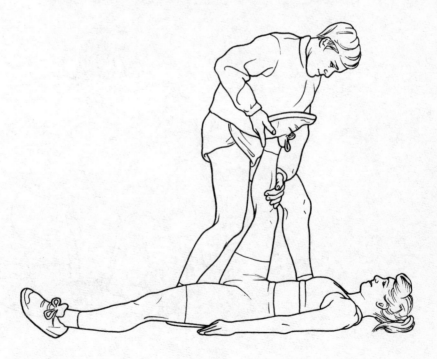

**PNF 12**   **Sitting inner thigh** *(short adductors)*

- The stretcher begins by sitting on the floor with the knees flexed and legs rotated outwards, with the soles of the feet together.
- The stretcher pulls the knees towards the floor by contracting the hip abductors (gluteus minimus and medius – part of the buttocks). This lengthens the short adductors to the current end of ROM.
- The partner kneels in front of the stretcher, placing hands on the inside of the stretcher's knees.
- The stretcher performs an isometric contraction of the short adductors for 6 seconds by attempting to bring the knees together. At the same time the partner resists the movement by applying equal and opposite force downwards using the hands.
- The stretcher relaxes for 6 seconds in this position. The partner then attempts to lower the stretcher's knees towards the floor, thereby increasing the stretch on the short adductors.
- Repeat this sequence of stretching from the new lengthened position up to 4 times, reducing repetitions when the required end ROM is achieved.

## PNF **13**   **Sitting inner thigh** *(long adductors)*

- The stretcher begins by sitting upright with both legs extended out in front and the hands on the floor placed behind the back to support the upright spinal position. The stretcher contracts the hip abductors (gluteus minimus and medius – part of buttocks) in order to take the legs outwards and astride. Ensure that there is no hip rotation – the kneecap should be pointing towards the ceiling. This position lengthens the long adductors to their end ROM.

- The partner sits opposite the stretcher, placing their feet on the calves of the stretcher and hands behind back to support the upright spinal position.

- The stretcher performs an isometric contraction of the long adductors for 6 seconds by attempting to move the legs closer together. At the same time the partner resists the movement by applying equal and opposite force to keep the legs in a static position.

- The stretcher relaxes for 6 seconds in this position. Then the stretcher lifts the buttocks just off the ground, slides the legs further apart and sits down, thereby increasing the stretch on the long adductors.

- Repeat this sequence of stretching up to 4 times, reducing repetitions when the required end ROM is achieved.

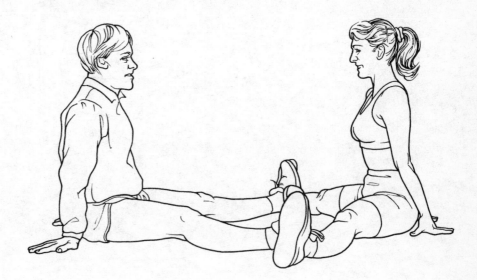

### Assisted straddle stretch *(long adductors)*

- Following this PNF stretch and while sitting with legs straddled, the following assisted static stretch can be performed:
- The stretcher and partner grasp each other's elbows. The stretcher should keep the back as straight as possible.
- The partner (in consultation with the stretcher) slowly pulls the stretcher towards him or herself until tension occurs in the adductors.
- The stretcher holds the stretch for 12–18 seconds, then relaxes. The partner then returns the stretcher slowly to sitting upright.
- This is repeated 2–4 times.

## PNF **14**  **Supine inner leg** *(long adductors)*

- The stretcher begins by lying on their back on the floor with body extended. The stretcher then contracts the hip abductors in order to move the legs as wide apart as comfortable. This position stretches the long adductors to their current end of ROM.
- The partner stands, with legs astride, in between the stretcher's legs. The partner's feet should be turned outwards slightly and placed underneath the knees of the stretcher.
- The stretcher performs an isometric contraction of the long adductors for 6 seconds by attempting to move the legs closer together. At the same time the partner resists the movement by applying equal and opposite force to retain the legs in a static position.
- The stretcher relaxes for 6 seconds in this position. The partner then gently assists the stretcher to move his or her legs further apart, thereby increasing the stretch on the long adductors.
- Repeat this sequence of stretching up to 4 times, reducing repetitions when the required end ROM is achieved.

*Note  It is common for abductor cramps to occur during this stretch. It is therefore sensible to stretch the abductors first.*

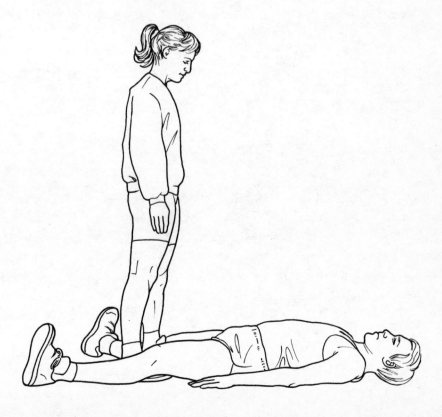

**PNF 15**   **Side leg lifts** *(long adductors)*

- The stretcher begins by lying on the left side with the body extended. They may rest the head on the left arm or use the left arm to prop the head up. Bend the left leg 90 degrees at the knee to stabilize the position. The thighs should be in alignment with the torso.
- The stretcher then contracts the hip adductors in order to lift the right leg up as far as comfortable without rotating the leg. This position stretches the right long adductor to the current end of ROM.
- The partner stands with one foot in front of the other for stability, holding the stretcher's right foot.
- The stretcher performs an isometric contraction of the long adductors for 6 seconds by attempting to move the leg down towards the floor. At the same time, the partner resists the movement by applying equal and opposite force to retain the leg in a static contraction.
- The stretcher relaxes for 6 seconds in this position. The partner then moves the stretcher's right leg higher until tension occurs in the muscle, thereby increasing the stretch on the long adductors.
- Repeat this sequence of stretching up to 4 times, reducing repetitions when the required ROM is achieved.

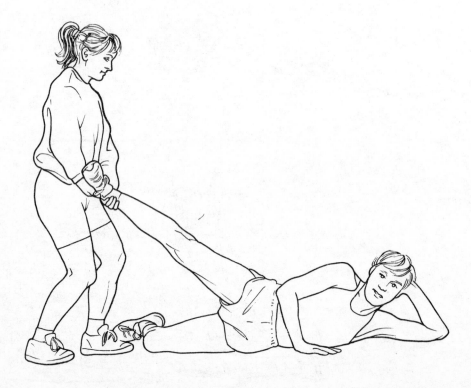

## PNF **16** **Prone quads** *(quadriceps)*

- The stretcher begins by lying face down on the floor with legs extended. They may rest the head on the hands for comfort.
- The stretcher bends the right leg at the knee, taking the heel towards the buttocks as far as possible. This position stretches the quadriceps to the current end of ROM.
- The partner kneels down and places one hand on the stretcher's right ankle and the other on the left hip.
- The stretcher performs an isometric contraction of the quadriceps for 6 seconds by attempting to push the right leg backwards towards the floor. At the same time, the partner resists the movement by applying equal and opposite force in order to retain the right leg in a static position.
- The stretcher relaxes for 6 seconds in this position. The partner then gently moves the heel further towards the buttocks, thereby increasing the stretch on the quadriceps.
- Repeat this sequence of stretching up to 4 times, reducing repetitions when the required ROM is achieved.

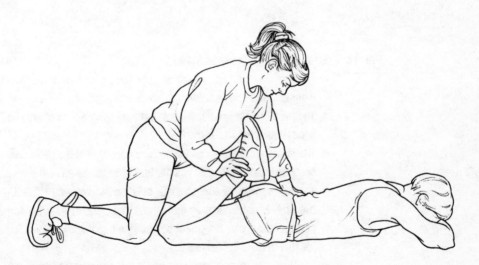

## PNF **17**    **Calf** *(gastrocnemius)*

- The stretcher begins by lying on back, then flexes the toes of the right foot as far as comfortable. This position stretches the gastrocnemius to the current end of ROM.
- The partner kneels and places one hand around the stretcher's right foot.
- The stretcher performs an isometric contraction on the calf for 6 seconds by attempting to point the toes forwards. At the same time the partner resists the movement by applying equal and opposite force in order to retain the foot in a static position.
- The stretcher relaxes for 6 seconds in this position. Then the partner gently moves the right foot further towards the shin, thereby increasing the stretch on the calf.
- Repeat this sequence of stretching up to 4 times, reducing repetitions when the desired ROM is achieved.

## PNF **18**    **Shin stretch** *(tibialis anterior)*

- The stretcher lies face up on the floor and points their toes. This position lengthens the tibialis anterior to the current end of ROM.
- The partner cups the left hand around the stretcher's right heel and the right hand around the top of the foot.
- The stretcher performs an isometric contraction of the tibialis anterior for 6 seconds by attempting to pull the foot towards the shin. The contraction should begin gently and gradually build up to maximum effort. **Do not hold breath** – breathe normally throughout PNF sequence. At the same time, the partner resists the movement by applying equal and opposite force to retain the foot in a static position.
- The stretcher relaxes for 6 seconds in this position. Then the partner points the stretcher's toes, thereby increasing the stretch on the shin.
- Repeat this sequence of stretching up to 4 times, reducing repetitions when the required ROM is achieved.

## PART 5

**Sport-specific Flexibility**

## AEROBICS

Since the early 1980s there has been a dramatic increase in supervised classes in exercise to music, usually called aerobics. Exercise-to-music classes include aerobics (high or low impact); aerobics using small apparatus such as elastic bands or hand weights; step aerobics; cardiofunk; and aeroskip. More recently there has been an upsurge in classes for special groups, including ante and post natal women and the older population (50 + ).

Exercise-to-music classes are more difficult to characterize than most sports as there are many different types of classes taught at different levels of intensity. Classes may be designed to improve or maintain different components of fitness, including cardio-respiratory, muscular endurance, flexibility, balance and co-ordination. Often classes do not improve cardio-respiratory fitness because the aerobic section of the class is not long enough or hard enough to elicit such development. In that case classes only maintain fitness, though they may yield health benefits. Therefore it is important for teachers to offer graded classes so that the beginner can progress to intermediate and then advanced level.

Exercise-to-music classes vary enormously in style, depending on the background of the teacher. At one end of the spectrum the style is athletic; at the other there is a mixture of dance and aerobics, such as cardiofunk. In the athletic style the movements are precise and work muscle groups specifically to improve muscular endurance. The dance oriented style includes 'entertainment moves': interesting creative movements that are fun to perform but do not have a specific fitness benefit in themselves.

Recently aerobics has become competitive, with national and world championships becoming established. This creates a new group of aerobic participants – the elite competitive – apart from instructors and recreational participants.

*Injuries*  The most common injuries in exercise-to-music classes include lower limb problems – often shin splints and knee pain – and lower back pain.

Shin splints is pain along the inner or outer edge of the shin-bone. It is an overuse strain, more common amongst people who exercise on a hard surface, such as concrete. The ideal flooring for aerobics is a wooden sprung floor. Good footwear is also vital in reducing the risk of lower leg injury.

Stretching exercises act as a preventative measure and enhance performance. In the case of the lower leg, the upper and lower calf muscles should be stretched during the warm-up section of all aerobic classes. It is also prudent for participants to be given the responsibility and freedom to stop and stretch out the lower leg muscles at any time during the class.

The knee is the most injury-prone of all the joints in the body. There are several precautions that can be taken to reduce the incidence of injury:

- ensure that the legs are not bent more than 90 degrees during squats or lunges;
- give participants low-impact options during high-impact sections of aerobics classes to allow individuals to work at appropriate intensities; and
- teach a variety of footwork throughout the class so that the knees are not stressed excessively in any one direction.

Step aerobics causes more knee injuries than any other form of aerobics. Instructors should be vigilant about adding variety in the stepping patterns, reconsider high-impact moves on the step, always emphasize good technique throughout the class and advise participants of the appropriate height of the step platform, depending on the height and ability of the participant.

Problems with the lower back are often related to poor posture. The teacher should remind participants about good posture throughout the class, whether they are standing, sitting or lying. Many of the floor exercises in an aerobics class require the back to be flat and the pelvis centred.

Participants should choose an appropriate class that suits their current level of fitness. If they are beginning exercise for the first time or following illness or injury, they should begin slowly (in terms of intensity) and build up fitness gradually.

**Instructors**    With the growth in exercise-to-music classes came the need to educate people to teach. In many countries there are a number of organizations that run short certificated courses for fitness and exercise teachers. Some instructors teach exercise-to-music classes as a hobby in the evening; for others – such as physical education teachers or staff who work in health clubs – aerobics is part of their full-time job; and there is a third category of instructors who teach aerobics full time. This latter group of individuals is particularly at risk of injury for a number of reasons. When injury occurs, it is difficult for the full-time freelance instructor to rest and allow the injury to heal, as aerobic classes are their sole income. Overuse injuries, including shin splints and voice problems, are common with the freelance instructor.

Freelance fitness and exercise instructors are advised to teach a variety of fitness and exercise classes at different intensities. If the overall intensity of the classes is still very high over the week, consider ways in which active participation can be reduced and verbal instruction increased. Remember that the class should be designed with the participants in mind – it is not a personal workout. To safeguard against voice problems, use a radio microphone wherever possible.

**Warm-up**   The warm-up should be thorough and tailored to suit class members and the particular type of class. Here is an example of a typical warm-up.

- Begin with rhythmic movements, such as marching on the spot with relaxed arm movements below the level of the shoulders, for about 5 minutes. This will gradually raise the heart rate.
- Next, perform some mobility exercises, such as those on pages 55–64. Mobility exercises will loosen up the joints.
- Now perform static stretching exercises, following the schedule below.
- Return to movements like marching and gradually increase the heart rate in preparation for the aerobic section of the class.

As in all sports, a cool-down is essential following an aerobics session. Gradually lower the intensity of the exercises to gradually lower the heart rate. When breathing and heart rate are close to resting rates, perform some static stretches similar to those in the warm-up.

### Aerobics flexibility schedule

19 Upper and lower back hug
25 Sitting spinal twist
33 Knee hug
40 Sitting one-legged ham stretch
49 Sitting inner thigh stretch
 8 Overhead stretch
27 Behind back chest stretch
 4 Bent arm stretch
 9 Triceps stretch

*Continues over*

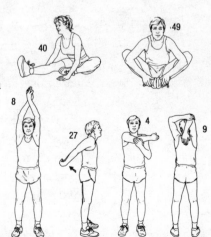

26 One-armed side stretch
34 Kneeling hip stretch
55 Standing quads
45 Feet apart ham stretch
48 Inner thigh lunge
58 Wall calf stretch
64 Bar stool stretch

## ATHLETICS

The central activities of athletics are running, jumping and throwing. These activities are also essential elements of many other sports. Consequently, we have covered the area in some detail, dealing separately with sprinting, distance running and jogging, jumping and throwing. If you participate in a sport that involves any of these activities, then you may wish to familiarize yourself with the advice in the relevant section.

**Sprinting**

Sprint performance is determined by an optimum combination of stride length and stride frequency. It is normal to find top-class athletes running 100 metres with fifty strides or less. Given that the sprint start requires a few short strides to accelerate the body over the first 30 metres, clearly at some stage the stride length is well over 2 metres (6.6 feet). Top-class sprinters can cover 2.5 metres (8.2 feet) per stride. Research has found that the optimum stride length is 2.3 to 2.5 times the leg length. Such a range of movement requires substantial flexibility in the flexors and extensors of the hips, knees and ankles (quadriceps, hamstrings, calves and iliopsoas muscles).

As well as the obvious requirements of dynamic flexibility in the muscles of the lower limbs, the sprinter needs to produce a large range of powerful movement at the shoulders. The role of the arms in sprinting is critical. They have a balancing and co-ordinating function. If you want your legs to be fast, then the arms have to be fast. It is impossible to run with fast legs and slow arms! The muscles of the upper limbs need to be strong and flexible.

**Injuries**  Powerful and dynamic sprinting actions can cause injury if muscular development is unbalanced. The most vulnerable areas are the lower limbs and lower back. In particular, hamstring pulls and tears are common. It is important that sprinters strengthen their hamstring muscles so that they can tolerate the large forces that are thrust through them. Sprinters must stretch their hamstrings on a regular basis to ensure that they can lengthen, and lengthen at speed.

**Warm-up**  A warm-up for a top-class sprinter before competition will take a long time. We have seen Linford Christie, the Olympic 100-metre champion, spend almost an hour preparing for a major championship event. The sprinter's warm-up will start with a very slow jog of about 10 minutes. It is followed by a series of static stretches as listed below. After the stretching the athlete should stride 40 to 60 metres, four or five times, at submaximal speeds. These strides have three functions. They rehearse sprint technique; they mobilize the appropriate muscles and joints; and they focus the athlete's mind on the specific movements they are about to perform. After the strides, the athlete should perform mobilizing exercises within the range achieved by the active stretches. If the athlete is at a competition, they should maintain the warmth of the muscles and the ROM by occasional mobilizing and stretching before the competition starts.

At the competition start, the athlete will use the available time to rehearse the sprint start and mentally focus upon their competitive strategy.

Occasionally athletes will introduce passive stretching into their warm-up, using a partner to assist. The advantage of passive stretching, in comparison with active stretching, is that it can enable a larger range of movement to be achieved, particularly in athletes who are chronically stiff. The disadvantage of passive stretching is that it normally requires a knowledgeable and experienced partner who may not be available at the competition or training venue.

### Sprinting flexibility schedule

23 Standing back curl
22 Lying back curl
37 Supine spinal rotation
25 Sitting spinal twist
20 Shoulder stretch
 8 Overhead stretch
 9 Triceps stretch
11 Lats stretch
 3 Arm press
34 Kneeling hip stretch
33 Knee hug
36 Lying gluteals stretch
42 Supine one-legged ham stretch
38 Sitting spinal hip rotation
50 Sitting elbows on knees stretch
48 Inner thigh lunge
43 Standing ham stretch
55 Standing quads
58 Wall calf stretch
63 Wall Achilles stretch

### Distance running and jogging

Analysis of the technique of distance runners reveals that, in comparison to sprinters, their muscles tend to move through a fairly small ROM. They also tend to repeat the same movements many times. For example, the gastrocnemius and soleus muscles of the calf, which flex and extend the ankle during running, move through a restricted range but do so about 3,000 times in a 5-kilometre (3-mile) run. The consequence of these repeated movements is that over time, the muscle becomes both short and tight.

The same problem affects most of the muscles involved in the propulsion phase of distance running. There is a similar problem in those muscles involved in **supporting** the body while running (**fixators**). The muscles of the lower back, which stabilize the spine, tend to become tighter. Over time, this can lead to poor posture and backache.

*Injuries*    Runners should remember that they are vulnerable to injury from two sources, apart from inflexibility. Firstly, the force that running generates is estimated as three times your body weight **in each stride**. Every individual has a different capacity to absorb the force, some good and some poor. In general, rigid feet are poor shock absorbers. Consequently runners with rigid feet must ensure that their training shoes are capable of absorbing shock. Runners also need to avoid training on hard surfaces over long periods of time. Varying the training surfaces on which you run. Use grass, roads, trails and tracks.

The second possible source of injury is biomechanical irregularity. Few of us are born with legs that are exactly equal in length and are without some minor defect. If you have small biomechanical irregularities, the repetitive nature of distance running can lead to tendon or muscle injury. A bow leg may lead to Achilles tendon injuries due to the excessive movement (pronation) at the foot. Runners who have recurrent injuries should visit a sports podiatrist to have a biomechanical assessment. Most biomechanical problems can be solved by using appropriate orthotics.

**Warm-up**  Runners need to use two different forms of warm-up. The first warm-up is to be used before a steady, low-intensity training run. The second warm-up is more comprehensive and should be used before fast training sessions and races.

A warm-up before a training run is divided into two sections. Firstly, complete the flexibility schedule below before you go for a run. If you have been sitting down for some hours before you exercise, your muscles will be cold and short. Stretching will accustom the muscles to the range of movement that running demands. Use the first 10 minutes of your run as the second part of your warm-up. Start the run slowly and gradually increase the pace. **Never start fast in a training run**.

Use the last 5 minutes of your training run as a cool-down (see page 37). At the conclusion of your run, the muscles will be warm and particularly receptive to flexibility training. Find time to stretch calves and hamstrings after a run.

If you are warming up for a **race** you should follow the following schedule.

- Jog for 5 to 10 minutes.
- Complete the flexibility schedule below.
- Complete 3 or 4 strides over 80 metres at a pace just faster than race pace.
- Jog slowly until the start of the race.

### Running flexibility schedule: before races

19  Upper and lower back hug
25  Sitting spinal twist
22  Lying back curl
37  Supine spinal rotation
33  Knee hug
42  Supine one-legged ham stretch
20  Shoulder stretch
 8  Overhead stretch
26  One-armed side stretch
 9  Triceps stretch
11  Lats stretch
34  Kneeling hip stretch

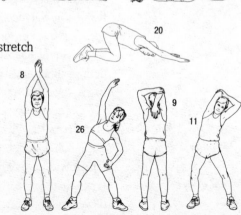

55  Standing quads
58  Wall calf stretch
63  Wall Achilles stretch

**_Running flexibility schedule:_**
**_before training_**

8  Overhead stretch
19  Upper and lower back hug
55  Standing quads
58  Wall calf stretch
63  Wall Achilles stretch
34  Kneeling hip stretch
33  Knee hug
42  Supine one-legged ham stretch

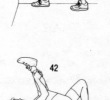

**Jumping**

World and national jumping records have been bettered over the years as athletes have improved their strength, speed and technique. Within each event there are a number of variations of technique. High jumpers who use the famous Fosbury flop are divided into 'power' floppers and 'speed' floppers. Power floppers tend to have a relatively slow and deliberate approach to the bar, and a powerful upward thrust of the arms and legs at take-off. Speed floppers run much faster to the bar and try to convert their fast horizontal momentum to upward momentum.

Variations in technique can also be seen in long jumpers. One group takes a long last stride before take-off in an attempt to run at speed off the take-off board. Another group deliberately shortens the last stride and sinks down to produce a powerful upward thrust of the arms and free leg.

**Injuries**

Training for jumping involves weight training, circuit training, running and sprinting. There is also a great deal of hopping and bounding involved in order to develop power. Power or 'fast strength' is defined as the ability to generate force quickly. Power exercises are potentially dangerous. **Athletes must be introduced to power exercises gradually over a number of years if injury is to be avoided.**

Jumpers tend to be injured in the foot, ankle and knee due to impact injuries and twisting of the take-off foot. Training must ensure that the muscles around these joints are strong so they can withstand the forces that jumping creates.

Flexibility training for jumpers is similar to that of sprinters. High jumpers need to have particularly good shoulder and lower back mobility to obtain the best position in clearing the bar.

**Warm-up**   A warm-up for jumpers should follow this pattern.

- Jog 2 to 3 laps of the track.
- Work through the flexibility schedule below.
- Run through 3 to 4 **relaxed** strides over 30 to 40 metres
- Complete mild mobilizing exercise within the ROM achieved through static stretching (see pages 64–105).
- Run two to three **fast** sprints over 30 metres.
- Set out check marks and embark on practice jumps.

### Jumping flexibility schedule

19  Upper and lower back hug
22  Lying back curl
37  Supine spinal rotation
20  Shoulder stretch
26  One-armed side stretch
 8  Overhead stretch
 9  Triceps stretch
11  Lats stretch
34  Kneeling hip stretch
33  Knee hug
42  Supine one-legged ham stretch
38  Sitting spinal hip rotation
43  Standing ham stretch
55  Standing quads
58  Wall calf stretch
63  Wall Achilles stretch

**Throwing**  The best throwers in the world are usually strong and athletic, with good balance. They also need an excellent throwing technique, as small changes in technique make a large difference in the distance that an implement can be thrown.

The physical elements that contribute to a good technique are **mobility** and **strength**. Mobility is required in the shoulders and hips. Good mobility in the shoulders will enable you to 'pull' on the implement over a long range. Mobility in the hips assists in the twisting or rotational movements that are required in most throwing events.

Throwers need a great deal of strength and power or 'fast strength'. Good throwers usually have a strong throwing arm that they can move quickly. The best throwers bring into action the large muscles of the legs and back in order to develop bigger forces in each throw. Training involves strengthening arms, legs and back, so throwers spend much time in the weights room.

**Injuries**  Amongst throwers, most injuries occur in the knees, lower back, shoulders and elbows. These injuries are often due to poor or erratic throwing and lifting techniques, muscle imbalance caused by a limited one-sided weight training programme, inadequate mobility, and inadequate levels of conditioning. To avoid injury you should:

- develop a safe, consistent lifting technique;
- strengthen legs, lower back, stomach and arms;
- establish a consistent throwing technique that will avoid extreme throwing positions;
- develop mobility and flexibility in back, hips and shoulders.

**Warm-up**  At each competition you will be told how much time you can have in the arena for practice throws before the competition starts. Your warm-up should start about 45 minutes before the first practice throw. You should:

- jog one to two laps of the track;
- embark on mobilizing exercises (see pages 55–64) within the existing range of movement to warm up the shoulder girdle;
- complete the flexibility schedule outlined below;
- introduce more vigorous and specific ballistic exercises;
- start your practice throws.

Equipped with mobility, strength and technique, you will throw further than you dreamed possible!

*Throwing flexibility schedule*

18 Upper back hug
19 Upper and lower back hug
26 One-armed side stretch
25 Sitting spinal twist
37 Supine spinal rotation
34 Kneeling hip stretch
42 Supine one-legged ham stretch
20 Shoulder stretch
 7 Wall shoulder stretch
 8 Overhead stretch
 3 Arm press
 4 Bent arm stretch
 9 Triceps stretch
11 Lats stretch
55 Standing quads
58 Wall calf stretch
63 Wall Achilles stretch

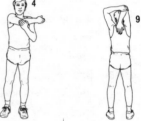

## BADMINTON

Badminton requires a high level of fitness. Elite players are well co-ordinated, have strong wrists and arms, and are able to jump high and move quickly about the court. Agility is very important. At international level, rallies can be fairly long and require the players to develop aerobic fitness. Given the importance of agility, the development of flexibility is particularly vital in badminton players. A stiff, inflexible player cannot hope to cover the court at speed.

*Injuries*  The main locations of injuries in badminton players are shoulders, calves, Achilles tendons and ankles. The knees and wrists are also vulnerable. Injuries are often due to an inadequate warm-up, lack of flexibility, and the development of only one side of the body. Injuries are occasionally due to

a lack of aerobic fitness that results in fatigue and causes the player to use desperate measures to scramble the shuttle back over the net. In these circumstances injury is almost inevitable.

The high physical demands of badminton mean that if you aspire to playing at a good level you must become fit and flexible. It also means that if you play 'social' badminton on a once-a-week basis, you are vulnerable to injury unless you warm up appropriately. Recreational badminton players should try to improve their physical condition by adding some general fitness training to their weekly schedule. Do not spend too much time practising one shot; this will lead to the overdevelopment of one group of muscles. Practice a variety of shots. Find time to add drills that develop speed and endurance rather than only working on skill and tactics.

***Warm-up*** Arrive at the sports centre 30 minutes before your court time. Spend 5 to 10 minutes on an aerobic activity to raise the temperature of your muscles. You could use a stationary bike or a rowing machine, or jog around the hall. Then:

- complete the flexibility schedule below;

- rehearse some shots without the shuttle, such as drop shots, clears, and serves;
- practice sideways, forwards and backwards running, agility and footwork;
- knock up with a partner.

### *Badminton flexibility schedule*

19 Upper and lower back hug
38 Sitting spinal hip rotation
 6 Prayer stretch
 7 Wall shoulder stretch
 8 Overhead stretch
 9 Triceps stretch
11 Lats stretch
13 Wrist pulls
15 Assisted wrist flexors
17 Angular rhomboids
 3 Arm press
26 One-armed side stretch
30 'U' chest stretch
48 Inner thigh lunge
55 Standing quads
42 Supine one-legged ham stretch
58 Wall calf stretch
63 Wall Achilles stretch

## BASKETBALL

Modern basketball is played at great speed and therefore requires players to be athletic. They need jumping ability, sprinting speed, endurance, agility and co-ordination. Training should be aimed at improving fitness as well as individual and team skills.

It is obvious from observing at competitions that many players try to rely entirely on their skill and are not as fit as the game demands. It is

particularly apparent in women's basketball, where the number of participants is relatively low, that fitness levels are poor. Players must be aware that increased fitness will enhance their skills and effectiveness on court.

***Injuries*** Inevitably, contact (traumatic) injuries occur. The most frequent sites of injury are ankles, knees, wrists and fingers. A thorough warm-up and good physical condition will reduce the probability of injury.

On occasions some basketball players suffer from shin splints. Shin splints can be caused by frequent contact with hard surfaces. Players with this condition should evaluate their training programme in order to reduce the number of contacts with the floor. They should also ensure that their shoes offer sufficient shock absorption.

Basketball players need good shoes to protect them from impact injuries and sprained ankles. Standard basketball boots offer some support and stability to the ankle. However, the ankle is very vulnerable in the game and players are advised to tape ankles to provide additional support. A sports physiotherapist will be able to advise players on how to tape ankles.

Injuries will occur when players are not sufficiently fit to maintain the pace required in the game. Tired players find that their skills and technique break down and it is then that they become susceptible to injury. Fitness training involving running, weight training, circuit training and flexibility should be used to ensure good all-round condition.

**Warm-up**
- Jog around the court slowly until you start to perspire, which will probably take between 5 and 10 minutes.
- Complete the stretching routine below.
- Rehearse your individual shooting, catching and dribbling skills.
- Rehearse team skills.
- Practise running with changes in direction, running sideways and footwork.

***Basketball flexibility schedule***

25 Sitting spinal twist
20 Shoulder stretch
26 One-armed side stretch
 8 Overhead stretch
 9 Triceps stretch
11 Lats stretch
27 Behind back chest stretch
55 Standing quads
42 Supine one-legged ham stretch
58 Wall calf stretch
63 Wall Achilles stretch

## BOWLS

Lawn bowls does not require participants to be super-fit but a certain amount of endurance and flexibility will enhance enjoyment and performance. Bowls is usually associated with mature participants (40 + ), though recruitment of young players is increasing. It is largely a

recreational and social activity but can be highly competitive. There is also an elite level in bowls, with national and world championships.

The act of delivering a bowl involves back swing, forward swing, release and follow-through. This involves adopting a balanced medium-low stance, leaning the torso forward from the hips, taking the arm behind the body close to the hips in preparation, and then smoothly swinging the arm forward to release the ball. This is accompanied by a smooth and controlled forward step and forward movement of the body. The natural completion of the delivery action is a flowing follow-through of the arm and body. The major muscles involved in this movement include those in the back, shoulders, arms and legs.

**Injuries**  The lower back is the most common site of injury; other less common injury sites include shoulders, forearm, knees and ankles. A warm-up consisting of mobility and stretching exercises will help to reduce the risk of injury.

Flexion with rotation of the back (bending forward and twisting) is the most stressful position for the discs, ligaments and muscles of the lower back. Therefore, if possible, lean forward with back straight and do not rotate the torso when swinging the arm to release the bowl. When bending the knees, ensure that the knee of the front leg is directly above the ankle;

do not allow the knee to go in front of the ankle as this places strain on the knee.

Aches and pains (delayed onset muscle soreness, or DOMS) are common after a game, usually experienced the following day. To alleviate and reduce the incidence of aches and pains, it would be beneficial to warm up prior to a game and stretch at the end.

**Warm-up**  Begin with a 5-minute walk, starting slowly and building up to a brisk pace. Then perform some mobility exercises, starting with the back working from head to toe. (see pages 55–64). Next follow the static stretching schedule below, which pays particular attention to the back and shoulders.

**Cool-down**  After a game it would be beneficial to ward off any stiffness by performing a few stretches like those in the warm-up.

### *Bowls flexibility schedule*

19 Upper and lower back hug
8 Overhead stretch
27 Behind back chest stretch
4 Bent arm stretch
26 One-armed side stretch
12 Wrist reach
15 Assisted wrist flexors
55 Standing quads
58 Wall calf stretch
64 Bar stool stretch

## CRICKET

Cricket is a game in which the pattern of exercise can be characterized as **intermittent and dynamic**. Fast bowling, fielding and batting (including running between wickets) requires the limbs to move extremely quickly and powerfully over large ranges of movement and for brief amounts of time. However, these small bursts of dynamic movement are often followed by periods of inactivity. A batsman may spend 2 or 3 minutes in the non-strikers' crease before being required to run a very sharp single. A fielder on the boundary may spend several minutes being relatively inactive before having to make a fast sprint to pick up and throw the ball a long way at great speed. **This particular pattern of activity and rest provides the optimum circumstance for injury.**

Softball and baseball share similar characteristics with cricket. They are dynamic sports which also have relatively long periods of inactivity or rest. Pitching, batting and fielding place similar demands on the muscles of the body in all three sports. Consequently, the cricket flexibility schedule is appropriate for participants in baseball and softball.

**Injuries**

Cricketers can suffer very serious injuries. It is not unusual for professional players to suffer injuries that hinder, shorten or halt their careers. Shoulders, back, knees and ankles are the sites of many problems.

Players are also liable to injury because their physical condition is poor and they play either without a warm-up or with a token gesture of some mobilizing exercises. Fast bowlers are particularly vulnerable. The poor running and bowling technique of many players also contributes to the incidence of strains, particularly in the shoulders and lower back.

***Warm-up***  As in other sports, the warm-up for cricket should work from the general to the specific. A 5-minute jog should be followed by the flexibility exercises in this section. After stretching, specific batting, bowling and fielding activities should be practised.

Fielders should stretch between overs. Bowlers **must** stretch extensively, particularly lower back, calves, hamstrings and shoulders, before bowling. Batsmen should use the time when they are not facing deliveries to stretch calves, hamstrings and adductors.

### *Cricket flexibility schedule*

19  Upper and lower back hug
22  Lying back curl
37  Supine spinal rotation
25  Sitting spinal twist
20  Shoulder stretch
26  One-armed side stretch
 8  Overhead stretch
 9  Triceps stretch
11  Lats stretch
 4  Bent arm stretch
 3  Arm press
34  Kneeling hip stretch
33  Knee hug
42  Supine one-legged ham stretch
38  Sitting spinal hip rotation
48  Inner thigh lunge
55  Standing quads
58  Wall calf stretch
63  Wall Achilles stretch

## CYCLING

Cycling comprises several disciplines, road and track being the main ones. There are also competitions in mountain biking, cyclo cross, stayer races (cycling behind a motor cycle) and triathlons. In the triathlon the athlete swims, cycles and runs.

Different types of bike are used for the different disciplines. Track bikes are very light, weighing about 6 kilograms. They do not have brakes or gear changes. Braking is carried out by using the banks of the track. The frames of these bikes are carbon fibre. A road bike is slightly heavier – about 9 kilograms (20 pounds) – and it has brakes and gears. The road bike has to balance lightness for speed with sufficient strength to withstand road conditions.

Improvements in cycling performances are sought through better training methods and technical developments of bicycles. Bike designers attempt to reduce the air resistance, rolling resistance and frictional forces in the transmission of power.

The training for cycling events is largely determined by the duration of the competition. Cycling events last between one and five minutes on the track and between two and four hours on the road. Triathletes compete in a 4-kilometre (2.5-mile) cycle and finish with a marathon run of 42 kilometres (26 miles).

Cycling is an endurance based sport. Training loads are heavy: cyclists will train up to 1,000 kilometres (620 miles) per week. To achieve top-class performances takes 8 years of training. Typically, cyclists train only on the bike and do very little alternative activity.

**Injuries**  Traumatic injuries occasionally happen when collisions occur. Such injuries are usually fairly predictable in both their cause and treatment. However, the most frequent types of cycling injuries are overuse injuries. The knee is particularly vulnerable. Overuse injuries can be expected when cyclists are turning the pedals between 80 and 120 times per minute for hours on end. Calves, lower back and parts of the quadriceps become very strong, whilst hamstrings and stomach muscles are relatively weak. The result is muscular imbalance, which is the cause of many cycling injuries.

Cyclists should spend time training to achieve muscular balance. Circuit training, stretching and weight training are ideal ways of counteracting the effects of cycling.

**Warm-up**  • Complete the flexibility schedule below.
• Mobilize the shoulders and back (see pages 55–64).
• Start the cycle training with slow cycling until the legs are warm.

After the cycle ride it is advisable to stretch the lower back, quadriceps, calves and hamstrings. Stretching after a training session will reduce stiffness in the muscles on the following day.

**Cycling flexibility schedule**

19 Upper and lower back hug
25 Sitting spinal twist
 8 Overhead stretch
35 Crossed-leg gluteals
27 Behind back chest stretch
 4 Bent arm stretch
 9 Triceps stretch
11 Lats stretch
34 Kneeling hip stretch

55  Standing quads
45  Feet apart ham stretch
58  Wall calf stretch
64  Bar stool stretch

# DANCE

There are many different forms of dance, including ballet, jazz, modern, contemporary, tap, ballroom, and the varied types of folk dancing.

All forms of dancing require balance, agility, co-ordination and technique. Elite dancers also require high levels of cardio-respiratory and muscular endurance to fulfil arduous timetables of class, rehearsals and performances. The execution of some forms of dance – such as ballet, contemporary and jazz – is enhanced by excellent ranges of flexibility, whereas ballroom dancing and folk dancing do not require such extreme ranges of movement.

**Injuries**  An adequate warm-up is vital to all forms of dance, to reduce the risk of injury and to enhance performance. However, some folk dancers ignore warming up and begin a class by rehearsing a dance. The result is lower leg injuries such as calf strains and problems with the Achilles tendon. Elite performers will take great care to warm up properly and will usually warm up by stretching thoroughly before a technique class begins, which in turn is the preparation before rehearsal.

Other common injury sites include hips and feet, particularly in association with turn out and pointe work in ballet. Many children begin ballet dancing at the age of 4 or 5, when the emphasis is on developing basic movement skills. A child up to the age of about 10 should be encouraged to work within their natural ROM, developing strength, balance and control throughout the range, and should not engage in forced stretching since a child's ligaments are immature and can easily be overstretched. Also it is very important that pointe work is not undertaken before the age of 10 as the bones are still growing; premature pointe work leads to foot problems later in life. A child should begin pointe work with a gradual, progressive programme of exercises developing over several years.

A good floor surface for all forms of dance is very important to eliminate aching calf muscles. A wooden sprung floor is best. Footwear

varies depending on the type of dance, but if possible some form of footwear should always be worn, giving support and protection to the foot during rehearsal.

**Warm-up**  A warm-up for dance should be appropriate to the particular form of dance. Ballet, jazz and contemporary dance tend to include warming up as part of the dance exercise technique at the beginning of a class. Beware of excessive bouncing at the end of ROM, especially when standing leaning forward in an effort to stretch the hamstrings (exercise 43). This particular stretching exercise should not be performed by anyone with back problems. If dancers cannot feel the stretch on the hamstrings, they should perform exercise 42 instead.

### Dance flexibility schedule

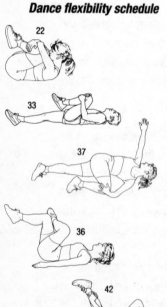

| | |
|---|---|
| 22 | Lying back curl |
| 33 | Knee hug |
| 37 | Supine spinal rotation |
| 36 | Lying gluteals stretch |
| 42 | Supine one-legged ham stretch |
| 38 | Sitting spinal hip rotation |
| 49 | Sitting inner thigh stretch |
| 52 | Sitting straddle |
| 26 | One-armed side stretch |
| 8 | Overhead stretch |
| 27 | Behind back chest stretch |
| 9 | Triceps stretch |
| 11 | Lats stretch |
| 48 | Inner thigh lunge |
| 55 | Standing quads |
| 43 | Standing ham stretch |
| 58 | Wall calf stretch |
| 63 | Wall Achilles stretch |
| 67 | Toe crush |
| 71 | Foot press |
| 69 | Ankle stretcher |
| 70 | Toes towards shin |

## FOOTBALL

Football (or soccer) is a sport that has high fitness requirements. Players need to have excellent sprinting speed over distances up to about 70 metres (76 yards). They require good jumping ability, good endurance, and some upper body strength. The game demands that players sprint and jump many times in a match, often with minimal recovery between efforts. Top-class players in mid-field positions can run more than 10 kilometres (6.2 miles) in a 90-minute game.

Your training programme should develop aerobic and anaerobic endurance, muscular strength and power, and sprinting speed. The best methods for developing these qualities are running, weight training and circuit training.

*Injuries*  The most prevalent injuries among football players are concentrated on the knees and ankles, calves and Achilles tendons, and hamstrings. Groin injuries also occur. Some of these injuries are due to contact between players, accidental or otherwise. However, many injuries are the result of inadequate flexibility. Repeated running, jumping and kicking causes tightness in calves and hamstrings. Without appropriate flexibility, injury is inevitable.

**Warm-up**  A football player requires a long and complex warm-up due to the many and varied physical demands imposed by the game. Players should warm up by light jogging for 5 to 10 minutes, then follow the flexibility schedule outlined below.

After completion of the flexibility schedule, run three or four sprints, with each sprint being slightly faster than the previous one, over distances of about 30 metres (33 yards). The final run should be close to, but not at, maximum speed. Select and practise mobilizing exercises for the trunk, hips and groin (see pages 55–64). Players should then introduce passing, shooting, ball control, heading and sideways running activities to their preparation. Finally, they should work on the specific skills and techniques of their particular position on the field.

### Football flexibility schedule

19 Upper and lower back hug
25 Sitting spinal twist
 8 Overhead stretch
27 Behind back chest stretch
42 Supine one-legged ham stretch
40 Sitting one-legged ham stretch
33 Knee hug
36 Lying gluteals stretch
55 Standing quads
58 Wall calf stretch
62 Flexed-foot calf stretch
63 Wall Achilles stretch
64 Bar stool stretch
65 Kneeling Achilles stretch

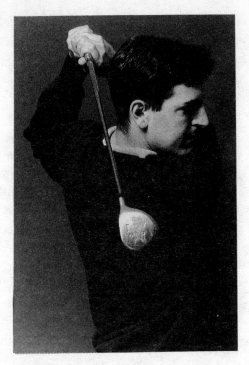

## GOLF

Golf is an increasingly popular recreational activity as well as a competitive and professional sport. Golf is characterized by short dynamic bursts of energy interspersed by walking. A fast round of golf may take 3 hours, though a more realistic estimate is $3\frac{1}{2}$ to 4 hours.

To play golf well does not require participants to be superfit, but a certain amount of endurance, strength and flexibility will enhance performance as well as enjoyment. Playing golf also involves good balance, rhythm, co-ordination, sound judgement of distance and other key variables (such as the effect of wind on the ball in flight or the bounce and run of the ball on landing), and the ability to focus upon the task immediately to hand. Sound technique and consistency of performance are critical so that the golfer can make appropriate decisions and produce the desired outcomes.

The full swing (backswing, downswing and follow-through) engages muscles in the legs, back, hips, shoulder girdle, arms and hands. There is considerable rotation of the shoulders and the hips, although these operate in different planes. From the top of the backswing, there is controlled acceleration of the arms and therefore the club, down to and well beyond the ball. The body should remain in balance throughout and after this sequence of movement.

In addition to the full swing, the golfer has to learn how to adjust their body stance swing in response to difficulties provided by the lie of the ball on the ground and any marked slope of the ground in the area of the ball. On occasions obstacles such as bushes, trees or artificial objects may restrict the swing. In addition to full shots (or swings) the golfer must learn to play specialist shots (such as play from sand bunkers, chip and pitch shots, and part-swing shots) and – most important of all – putting on and around the greens and where accuracy is essential.

The successful golfer will not necessarily be a great all-round athlete but he/she needs to be free from injury. Maintenance of sound physical condition and purposeful practice and play can assist the development of performance. The serious competitive golfer in a strokeplay competition may have to play four rounds in two or three days or more commonly two rounds in a day. Matchplay competitions make similar demands on players.

The golf drive involves muscles in the back, waist, shoulder girdle and arms. Obviously it is an asymmetric movement and therefore it is important to strengthen both sides of the body in training.

**Injuries** Golf is not usually considered an energetic sport, but golfers do get injured. The most common injuries sustained whilst playing golf are muscular strains and sprains in wrists, back, elbows and knees. A study of professional golfers (McCarrol & Grice, 1982) found a greater incidence of injury on the left side of the body. In order of frequency, injuries occurred to the wrist, back, left hand, left shoulder, left knee and left thumb. These injuries reflect the asymmetry of golf and indicate that a conditioning programme should strengthen both sides of the body. **Conditioning** for golf includes the development and maintenance of reasonable aerobic fitness, muscular endurance and flexibility.

Some studies on the incidence of golf injuries have found that elite players (professionals and good amateurs) sustain a higher number of wrist injuries compared to amateur golfers, where the back was the most frequent injury. Excessive play or practice and poor golf mechanics are the reasons usually given by players for their injuries. Amateur golf players might also reduce the incidence of lower back injury by performing warm-up exercises and avoiding carrying or pulling golf bags awkwardly.

**Warm-up** Begin by walking or light jogging for 5 minutes, then perform some mobility exercises (see pages 55–64) to gently raise the body temperature in preparation for stretching and for the game ahead. Now perform static stretching exercises, concentrating on the back forearm and shoulders (see schedule below). Begin golf practice by putting then hitting chip and pitch shots, followed by part-swing shots before progressing to full shot practice.

**Cool-down**  At the end of the game it is advisable to perform some stretching exercises to reduce the incidence of muscular soreness. This is especially useful for the older golfers.

**Golf flexibility schedule**

19  Upper and lower back hug
25  Sitting spinal twist
37  Supine spinal rotation
42  Supine one-legged ham stretch
20  Shoulder stretch
26  One-armed side stretch
 8  Overhead stretch
27  Behind back chest stretch
 9  Triceps stretch
11  Lats stretch
17  Angular rhomboids
12  Wrist reach
15  Assisted wrist flexors
55  Standing quads
58  Wall calf stretch
63  Wall Achilles stretch

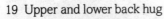

## HOCKEY

In the last decade, hockey has been transformed by the proliferation of artificial grass pitches. The game is now fast and unrelenting. The ball travels from one end of the pitch to the other in a few seconds and is rarely out of play for long. Players find that they need high levels of fitness to prevent their skills from breaking down when they become tired. Hockey players need agility, co-ordination, speed and endurance. All of these are enhanced by increased flexibility.

**Injuries**  The main sites of injury are the lower back, calf and Achilles tendon, and knee. Hamstring and groin injuries also occur. Players often receive bruises to all parts of the body, which means it is vital to wear shin guards when playing hockey.

Training for hockey should include individual skills work, team plays and fitness activities. The best time to concentrate on fitness training is in the non-competitive phase of the year. Try to develop a good level of endurance and speed **before** the season begins. During the season you can then simply maintain the level that you have achieved by playing and training.

**Warm-up**
- Jog for 5 minutes
- Complete the flexibility schedule below
- Run three fast, but not maximum speed, strides over 30 metres (33 yards)
- Rehearse turning whilst running backwards, sideways etc
- Practice individual skills, such as dribbling, shooting and passing
- Rehearse set plays, such as short corners
- Run two very fast sprints over 25 metres (27 yards)
- Keep warm by jogging until the start of the game

## Hockey flexibility schedule

19 Upper and lower back hug
22 Lying back curl
37 Supine spinal rotation
36 Lying gluteals stretch
20 Shoulder stretch
26 One-armed side stretch
 8 Overhead stretch
 9 Triceps stretch
11 Lats stretch
48 Inner thigh lunge
45 Feet apart ham stretch
55 Standing quads
58 Wall calf stretch
64 Bar stool stretch

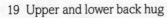

## MARTIAL ARTS

There are many forms of martial art, each type emphasizing a particular combination of skills. For example, karate is a system of fighting using the hands and feet to deliver powerful kicks, punches and strikes. The main styles of Japanese karate are shotokan, goju ryu, shito ryu and wado ryu. Other styles include shotokai, shukokai and kyokushinkai. The latter style is Korean, as is tae kwondo. Shotokan uses strong stances with an emphasis on generating maximum power, while in goju ryu students adopt higher stances than in shotokan and incorporate many circular movements. In shito ryu the movements tend to be crisper and shorter than in shotokan, and lighter and quicker than in goju ryu. Wado ryu is often described as a graceful and fast style which focuses on sophisticated evasion techniques.

Many types of karate exhibit dynamic, aggressive, precise, direct movements that are practised in sequences called kata, whilst other martial arts, such as aikido and tai chi, utilize softer, slower and more continuous movements. Shoringi kempo and kendo are yet another group of martial arts. These styles are more gymnastic; in kendo, poles are used to simulate the use of swords.

Each form of martial art requires its own specific combination of physical characteristics, including strength, flexibility and endurance. Other aspects of performance in martial arts include agility, balance, co-ordination and speed control. As the level of performance increases, high levels of cardio-respiratory fitness, strength and flexibility are desirable. Extreme flexibility around the pelvis is required for all forms of martial arts. This needs to be accompanied by high levels of strength in order to execute certain movements and maintain stability around the joints.

**Injuries**   The most frequent injuries include back pain and knee, wrist and hand, ankle, trunk and hip and groin injuries. Contact and poor technique are often cited as prime causes of injury in martial arts. Some of the muscular strains could be prevented through flexibility training designed to increase the ROM. This can provide an element of safety when dynamic movements venture close to or beyond current ROM.

**Warm-up**   Begin by slowly jogging for 5 minutes to gently increase the body temperature. Then perform mobility exercises to continue raising the heart rate and body and muscle temperature. Begin mobility exercises (see pages 55–64) in the order prescribed, beginning with the back exercises, then working from the head to feet. Add leg swinging exercises into this section, as all forms of martial arts involve an emphasis on hip mobility.

*Leg swinging exercises*
- Begin standing upright, with feet parallel, hip width apart. This exercise may be performed by yourself or by holding onto a partner's shoulder for balance and support.
- Raise the right leg forwards and upwards as far as is comfortable and then return to the floor.
- Perform the leg swings 8 times.

*Note  Do not swing the leg beyond the comfortable range. Remember, you are still warming up. Keep the supporting leg straight as the other leg is lifted up.*

*Alternatives*
- With the feet in the same position, raise the right leg directly to the right side, keeping the leg and foot parallel, and then return to the floor.
- With the feet still in the same position, lift the leg directly behind, trying to keep the torso still.
- These three leg swings can be repeated with the feet and hips rotated outwards as far as comfortable.

Now perform stretching exercises in the following schedule, paying special attention to muscles in the shoulder girdle, back, and surrounding the hips.

Martial arts at the highest levels require extreme flexibility, so PNF stretches should be performed on a regular basis. As in most sports, it is ideal if fitness increases as the skill level of the performer increases.

**Martial arts flexibility schedule**

22 Lying back curl
33 Knee hug
37 Supine spinal rotation
42 Supine one-legged ham stretch
36 Lying gluteals stretch
26 One-armed side stretch
 8 Overhead stretch
27 Behind back chest stretch
 9 Triceps stretch
11 Lats stretch
38 Sitting spinal hip rotation
49 Sitting inner thigh stretch
52 Sitting straddle
48 Inner thigh lunge
55 Standing quads
58 Wall calf stretch
63 Wall Achilles stretch
67 Toe crush
69 Ankle stretcher
70 Toes towards shin
71 Foot press

## NETBALL

Netball is an energetic game demanding high levels of endurance, speed, agility and moderate levels of muscular strength and flexibility. On court the players are often characterized by a low stance with the legs bent and the weight centred equally between feet. This is to allow for high speed changes in direction. It is primarily a women's sport in the UK, but recreational participation by men has become more popular in recent years. In Australia, netball is the most popular sport among women.

Conditioning for most sports will be structured in at least two phases, differing in the competitive season and the off-season.

Aerobic fitness can be developed through a variety of modes. Running is the most appropriate for netball, but other activities – such as swimming, cycling and rowing – will also develop endurance. It is particularly important that the duration and intensity of activity are appropriate so that the athlete makes improvement. After a reasonable aerobic base is developed, the athlete should concentrate on developing speed. Alongside the development of aerobic and anaerobic fitness, the netball player can work on flexibility, agility and ball handling skills.

***Injuries*** The most common injuries sustained by netball players are sprained ankles and fingers and wrist trauma. Other less frequent injuries occur in knees, shoulders, neck and back. Many injuries to the hand are sustained when the ball is caught at an awkward angle.

There are precautions that can be taken to reduce the risk of injury in netball, including an adequate warm-up, use of good footwear and a good floor surface for training.

It is important to wear training shoes that are designed for the demands of netball. They should provide support for movement in all directions as netball is a very agile game. Cushioning in the ball of the foot is especially important for shock absorption, since players will be landing from jumps and will for most of the game be on the forefront of the foot. Ideally, netball should be played on a sprung floor but if playing on a hard surface, try to mix play on different surfaces to avoid developing problems such as shin splints.

***Warm-up*** Begin by doing an easy light jog around the court for 5 minutes, followed by mobility exercises and then stretching exercises. To complete the warm-up, jog around the court again.

Following the warm-up, netball training generally involves ball skill practice, agility skill practice (such as shuttle sprints and dodging) and then whole team manoeuvres are performed and finally a game.

Mobility exercises for the whole body should be performed, beginning with the back, and then working from head to toe. Pay particular attention to shoulder and back (see pages 55–64).

All major leg muscles should be stretched, as well as shoulders and forearms. See the schedule below.

**Cool-down** At the end of a game it is beneficial to perform some static stretching exercises. Stretch the calf muscles (gastrocnemius and soleus), using a wall for support. Other stretches may be performed sitting and lying on the floor, which is relaxing after an energetic game of netball.

*Netball flexibility schedule*

19 Upper and lower back hug
33 Knee hug
37 Supine spinal rotation
42 Supine one-legged ham stretch
26 One-armed side stretch
 1 Neck flexion
 8 Overhead stretch
27 Behind back chest stretch
 9 Triceps stretch
11 Lats stretch
17 Angular rhomboids
12 Wrist reach
15 Assisted wrist flexors
38 Sitting spinal hip rotation
49 Sitting inner thigh stretch
52 Sitting straddle
48 Inner thigh lunge
55 Standing quads
58 Wall calf stretch
63 Wall Achilles stretch

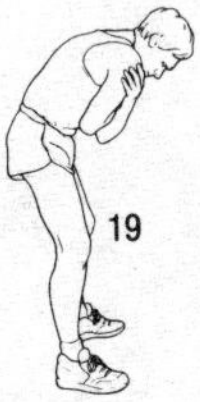

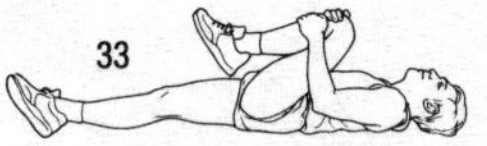

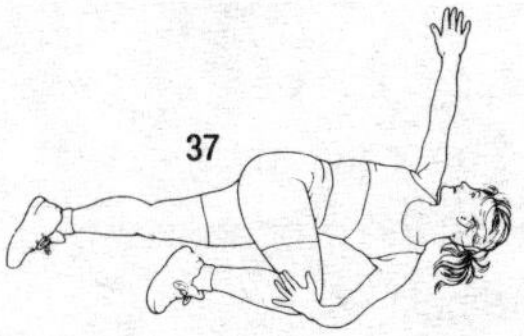

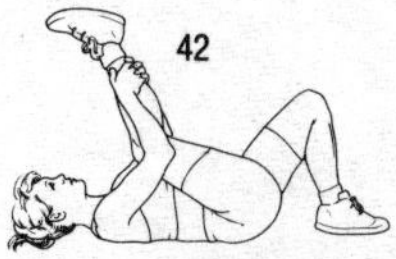

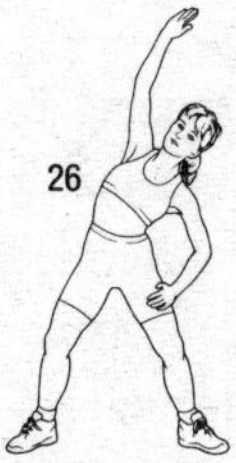

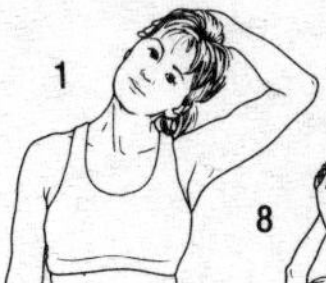

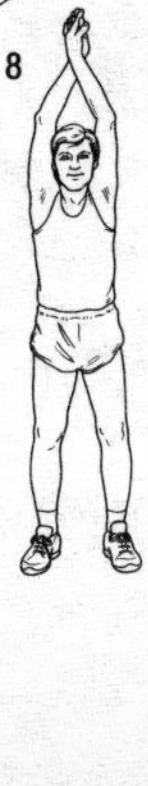

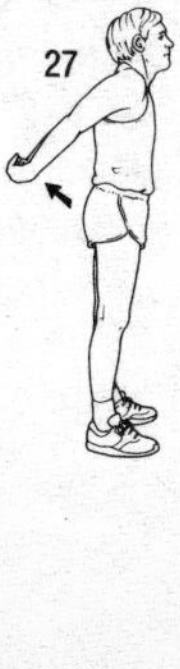

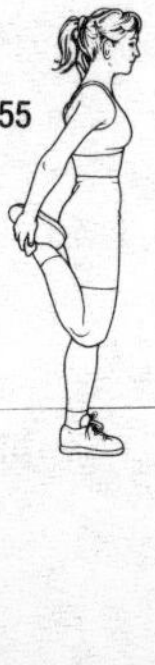

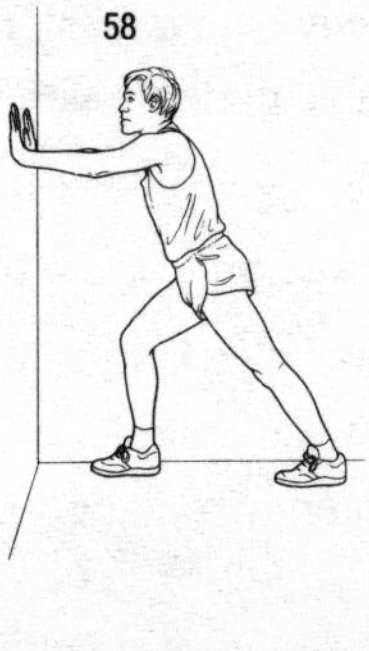

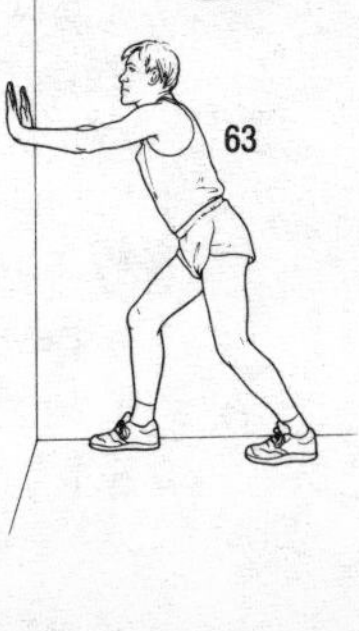

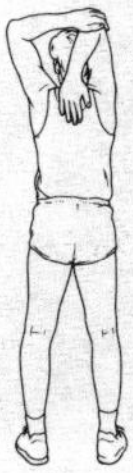

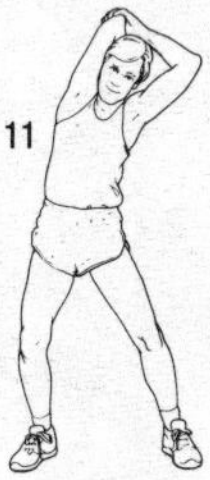

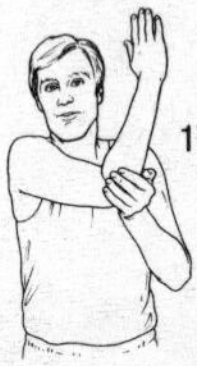

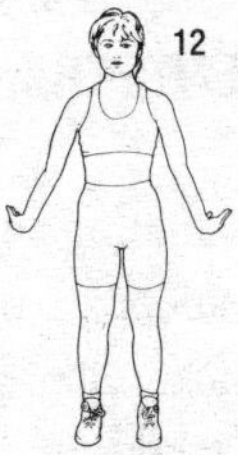

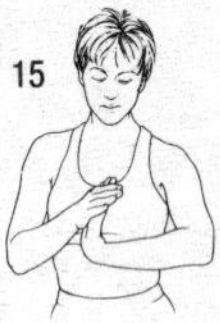

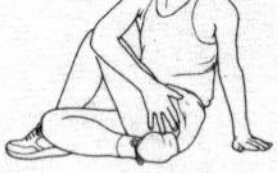

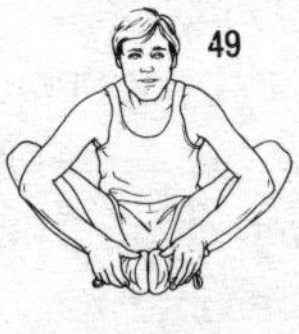

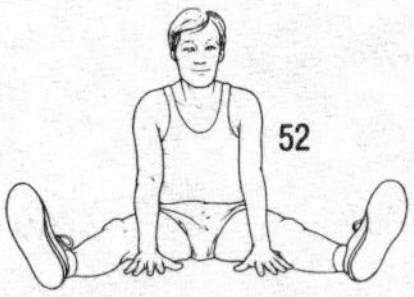

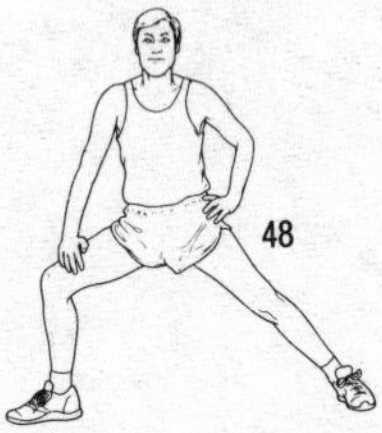

## ORIENTEERING

Orienteering shares many features with distance running. The best orienteers are usually outstanding distance runners. Consequently, the physical training for the two sports is similar. And so are the problems! At the University of Edinburgh we have seen some of the best young orienteers in the United Kingdom and advised them on both training and injury prevention.

Orienteers often run over difficult terrain during training and competition. The effect of running in these conditions is that they tend to become inflexible, lacking in muscular strength and **relatively** poor at track running or road running. If you wish to improve your running speed it is important to run at a high intensity for a reasonable time at least once a week to improve the oxygen supply to the muscles. It is difficult to run at a consistently high intensity when running on undulating terrain or through variable undergrowth. Use cross-country races to develop speed. Other training tips include:

- Introduce circuit training and weight training into your programme to develop a balance in muscles;
- Ensure that you conduct at least one session each week of stretching;
- Run one interval training session each week; and

- Run one session of 20 minutes each week at your best 10-kilometre (6-mile) race pace.

**Injuries**

Orienteers tend to develop the same injuries as distance runners. The calf, knee and lower back are particularly vulnerable. Specific to this sport are ankle injuries, which account for about 18 per cent of the total number of orienteering injuries seen at the University of Edinburgh Sports Injury Clinic.

**Warm-up**

It is advisable to adopt two forms of warm-up. The first warm-up should be used before easy training runs and the second before competition and fast training runs. The first warm-up provides the minimum preparation for exercise; the second is more thorough and prepares you for hard competitive exercise and arduous training sessions.

*Before easy training runs*

You should follow this schedule:

- Stretch according to the second schedule below.
- Go for your run but start slowly and run easily over the first 7 minutes.
- On return, stretch calves and hamstrings.

*Before races and interval training sessions*

- Jog for 10 to 15 minutes.
- Complete the flexibility schedule below.
- Run three or four fast strides over 60 to 80 metres.
- Jog and walk to keep moving until the start of the competition.

**Orienteering flexibility schedule**

*Before competitions*

19  Upper and lower back hug
22  Lying back curl
37  Supine spinal rotation
33  Knee hug
42  Supine one-legged ham stretch
66  Lower leg stretch
20  Shoulder stretch
 8  Overhead stretch
 9  Triceps stretch
27  Behind back chest stretch
34  Kneeling hip stretch
*Continues over*

55 Standing quads
58 Wall calf stretch
63 Wall Achilles stretch

*Before easy training runs*
58 Wall calf stretch
63 Wall Achilles stretch
66 Lower leg stretch
42 Supine one-legged ham stretch
57 Prone quads
37 Supine spinal rotation
 8 Overhead stretch
70 Toes towards shin

## ROWING, CANOEING AND KAYAKING

Rowing, canoeing and kayaking are obviously different sports, but there is a similarity in the functional demands on participants. Whether you are a competitive or a recreational participant, your enjoyment can be enhanced by improving your fitness, including flexibility. Adequate flexibility can enhance performance and reduce the incidence of injury.

Rowing, which incorporates a sliding seat, is considered to be one of the best forms of aerobic exercise, working muscles in the legs, arms and torso. It makes demands on the entire body, giving a complete workout without the hazards of shin splints or sore knees.

Canoeing normally involves the paddler kneeling, or half kneeling and half sitting on a seat. The legs are therefore working statically to maintain balance and control. This has implications for training and conditioning for this sport. Another characteristic of canoeing is that in most disciplines,

the canoeist only paddles on one side of the canoe. This one-sided aspect is an important consideration when planning a conditioning programme. Again canoeing is an aerobic activity, with arms and torso moving continuously and the legs acting as a stabilizer.

Kayaking involves paddling from a sitting position, using a double bladed paddle, providing an even upper body workout. The rhythmic action of paddling involves the arms and torso working continuously. An important aspect of paddling is the rotation of the torso on each forward placement of the blade.

**Injuries**  The most common injuries occur in the lower back, shoulders and forearms. Back problems are sometimes caused by an inadequate warm-up; in the case of canoeing, paddling only on one side can lead to muscle imbalance. Canoeists are advised to perform regular conditioning exercises, strengthening both sides of the body. Teenage enthusiasts are encouraged to paddle on both sides of the boat so that they don't build up a strength bias.

Kayaking can often lead to a sore bottom and coccyx because of the static sitting position. There is no easy answer to prevent this happening but you can stretch the buttocks and the lower back afterwards.

Injuries are sometimes caused by poor technique. In rowing, the flexible thoracic spine is often overworked rather than using the combined power of the thighs, hips and lower back.

Warming up is often neglected in all of these sports. This is understandable on cold early mornings, when you are desperate to get paddling or rowing to generate some heat. However, it is more important to warm up thoroughly on these cold mornings to avoid injury.

Conditioning is an important aspect of rowing, canoeing and kayaking, whether participants are recreational or competitive. A high level of aerobic fitness, muscular strength and endurance plus adequate flexibility can lead to increased performance and enjoyment and less injuries.

**Warm-up**

If possible, go for a brief, easy jog to generate body heat and gradually increase circulation of blood. Then perform mobility exercises (see pages 55–64) to gently lubricate joints and move major muscle groups. Start with the back, and then work from head to toe. If you are outside on a cold day, lying on the ground is inappropriate, so miss out sitting or lying down exercises. Then perform stretching exercises, paying particular attention to the shoulders, back, hip flexors and thighs.

**Rowing, canoeing and kayaking flexibility schedule**

19 Upper and lower back hug
22 Lying back curl
33 Knee hug
37 Supine spinal rotation
42 Supine one-legged ham stretch
35 Crossed-leg gluteals
8 Overhead stretch
27 Behind back chest stretch
4 Bent arm stretch
9 Triceps stretch
11 Lats stretch
17 Angular rhomboids
12 Wrist reach
15 Assisted wrist flexors
55 Standing quads
58 Wall calf stretch
64 Bar stool stretch

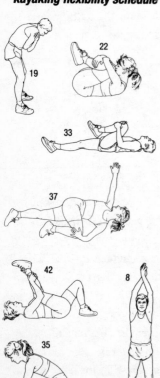

## RUGBY

The game of rugby offers a variety of physical challenges to participants. Forwards require substantial strength in the upper body, combined with powerful legs for driving in the scrum. Backs need great sprinting speed but also the upper body strength to make and withstand tackles. All players need speed, endurance and good ball handling skills. Elite rugby players borrow training methods from track and field athletes to meet the increasing demands of their sport.

Players can improve their endurance through running, cycling, and using rowing ergometers and other aerobic training equipment. Strength is best developed through weight training. Power and sprinting speed can be honed through plyometrics – fast running and sprinting drills. Players should consider the requirements of their position and organize the training accordingly.

**Injuries**    Injuries in rugby are evenly distributed throughout the body. Ankles, knees, backs, shoulders, calves and hamstrings are all vulnerable. Many injuries are caused through impact, either with another player or the ground. However, many are caused by lack of adequate or appropriate preparation. It is essential that rugby players work at flexibility exercises because the game itself, and the physical preparation for the game, will develop short tight muscles.

It is noticeable that many sports injury clinics treat a disproportionate number of rugby injuries during the pre-season period. Much pre-season rugby training is too intensive for players who have had a complete break in the off season. If you wish to avoid injury and improve your performances on the field, you should maintain some training during this period. Try to maintain aerobic fitness and develop strength during the non-competitive phase of the year. By arriving to start pre-season training in reasonable condition, you will have a platform from which to build new fitness levels.

**Warm-up**    The warm-up for a complex and physically demanding game like rugby will require at least an hour. Stretching, individual skills practice, group skills practice, team strategy and psychological preparation are the necessary components for a competition warm-up. You should therefore aim to arrive at the venue one and a half hours before kick-off to allow time to change and examine the pitch conditions. We suggest that you:

- Jog for 5 to 7 minutes;
- Complete the flexibility schedule below;
- Run three to four acceleration runs at sub maximal pace over 30 metres;
- Practise individual skills;
- Practise group and team skills;
- Return to dressing room for team talk and psychological preparation;
- Maintain ROM achieved through jogging, static and light ballistic stretching;
- Return to pitch and run two sub-maximal and two fast sprints over 20–25 metres;
- Complete mobilizing exercises (see pages 55–64); and
- Maintain physical condition until kick-off by jogging.

***Rugby flexibility schedule***

19   Upper and lower back hug
22   Lying back curl
37   Supine spinal rotation
36   Lying gluteals stretch

42 Supine one-legged ham stretch
20 Shoulder stretch
26 One-armed side stretch
8 Overhead stretch
9 Triceps stretch
11 Lats stretch
4 Bent arm stretch
28 'W' chest stretch
48 Inner thigh lunge
55 Standing quads
58 Wall calf stretch
64 Bar stool stretch
62 Flexed-foot calf stretch

## SKIING

Skiing can be divided into alpine skiing and cross-country skiing. The physiological demands are quite different for the two types, so preparation should match the appropriate demands.

**Cross-country skiing**    Although the vast majority of participants are recreational, cross-country ski racing and biathlon are Olympic sports. Cross-country skiing is usually regarded as requiring high levels of physical fitness, as it is a whole body sport with the arms and legs in constant motion. Certainly it makes the activity more pleasurable if you are able to ski easily up hills, without gasping for breath. However, participants are able to pace themselves at a comfortable rate, varying from walking pace to fast running pace. Cardio-respiratory fitness should be advanced to match technical skiing ability. If you are ski touring with a pack on, the need for good physical fitness is greater.

Elite skiers require very high levels of cardio-respiratory fitness and

excellent muscular strength endurance. Flexibility is very important to reduce the risk of injury and improve performance by enabling the skier to increase the length of each stride or glide.

**Injuries**    The most common injuries in cross-country skiing are to the knee, followed by shoulders, back, groin and calves. The incidence of some of these injuries could be reduced by regular participation in a conditioning programme plus warming up immediately prior to skiing.

**Warm-up**    Ideally, a warm-up would begin with some mobility exercises (see pages 55–64) before putting on the skis, followed by some stretching exercises covering the whole body (see schedule below), since the activity uses both arms and legs. If possible it is best to begin the day skiing on flat terrain to continue warming up the body gradually. If muscle soreness develops whilst skiing, it is best to stop immediately and stretch out the muscle concerned. It is normally the calf, thigh or hip flexors that become sore. At the end of the day's skiing it is advisable to stretch again, especially all major leg muscles plus back and arms.

**Alpine skiing**    Down-hill skiing is particularly taxing on the thigh muscles, which are continually contracting. Cardio-respiratory fitness is of less importance than in cross-country skiing, but muscular strength and endurance is of prime importance. A warm-up before venturing onto the slopes is very important to safeguard against injury. It is important to remember that in cold temperatures, muscles are less efficient, so warming up exercises before, during and after skiing are very important. It is surprising how many people completely disregard warming up, then wonder later why they are feeling so stiff.

**Injuries** The most common injuries (over 50 per cent) in alpine skiing are knee injuries. Other less common injuries include shoulder injuries, back pain, and wrist, hand, neck and foot injuries. Knee injuries are often caused by a combination of ill-prepared physical conditioning, poor technique and unfortunate falls. The less common injuries are nearly always caused by impact on falls.

**Warm-up** Many recreational skiers go on ski holidays with poor physical conditioning and often experience aches and pains after the first two days. Perform some mobility exercises (pages 55–64) first to gently increase the body temperature and then follow up with some stretching exercises, especially on the thigh and calf muscles. Once the legs are clicked into position in the boots, the position of the leg (bent and leaning forward) means that the soleus is constantly in a stretched position. Choose an easy run to go down (relative to your current technical ability) to continue the ski warm-up. If the body gets very cold, stop and warm up before continuing. This is especially important mid-afternoon, when the sun disappears behind a mountain and the temperature falls rapidly. After a long ride on a lift, peripheral body temperature cools rapidly and mobility and stretching exercises are advised before descending.

Stretching after a day's skiing helps to ward off muscle soreness. Stretch the shoulders, back and all major muscles in the legs.

### Skiing flexibility schedule

19 Upper and lower back hug
 8 Overhead stretch
27 Behind back chest stretch
26 One-armed side stretch
 9 Triceps stretch
11 Lats stretch
 4 Bent arm stretch
34 Kneeling hip stretch
55 Standing quads
45 Feet apart ham stretch
*Continues over*

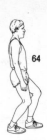

## SQUASH

Squash is a game that requires agility, co-ordination, technique and an excellent competitive temperament. Elite squash players also need to have great endurance. Top-class squash matches can last for 90 minutes or longer, with very long rallies and short recovery intervals. Players also need to be dynamic and capable of sudden quick movements over very short distances. The combined speed and endurance demands of the game require top-class squash players to be very fit.

**Injuries**    Recreational squash players tend to have relatively brief rallies, which are fairly dynamic, interposed with incomplete rest periods. The intensity of the game and speed of the movements is often high when compared to the fitness level of the players. These characteristics suggest that an adequate warm-up is vital if the risk of injury is to be reduced. Unfortunately, the conventional preparation for a squash match is normally limited to five minutes of court work to warm up the ball!

Incomplete preparation will leave the player susceptible to pulls, strains and even tears of the calf muscles and Achilles tendons. Players also need to be aware that their tendons and muscles decrease in elasticity as they become older. consequently squash players who are over 25 years of age **must** stretch before playing. Rupture of the Achilles tendon is not an unusual squash injury. A serious injury of this nature will require 6 to 8 weeks in plaster followed by 16 weeks' rehabilitation.

The hard surfaces of a squash court can lead to muscular soreness. Constant jarring may result in sore calves and lower back pain. Players must use adequate shoes. A good pair of squash shoes will be non-sliding, well cushioned under the heel and instep and have some reinforcement around the toe as protection from the dragging action that players adopt with their rear foot.

**Warm-up**    An adequate warm-up for squash would initially involve 5 to 10 minutes of
*Stage 1*    aerobic activity. Players who play in a sports centre could exercise on a stationary bike or treadmill to raise the temperature of their muscles by light aerobic work. If there is no alternative, a slow jog around the court will be sufficient. Follow the jog with the schedule of exercises below. Most players would need to concentrate on calves, buttocks, gluteals, lower back and shoulders.

*Stage 2*    The next stage of the warm-up is sport specific. Players should go on court and practise ghosting (rehearsing shots and movements without the ball). Then run four shuttle sprints from the back court to the front well. Finally, spend the last part of your warm-up with your opponent, warming up the ball. The overall warm-up for a competitive match will take between 20 and 30 minutes. If you arrive late for your court time **you must stretch**. Without stretching you will risk incurring a major injury.

**Squash flexibility schedule**    19  Upper and lower back hug
22  Lying back curl
*Continues over*

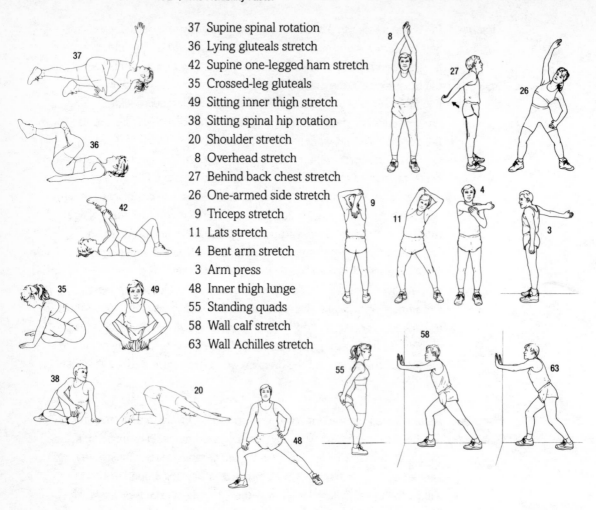

37 Supine spinal rotation
36 Lying gluteals stretch
42 Supine one-legged ham stretch
35 Crossed-leg gluteals
49 Sitting inner thigh stretch
38 Sitting spinal hip rotation
20 Shoulder stretch
8 Overhead stretch
27 Behind back chest stretch
26 One-armed side stretch
9 Triceps stretch
11 Lats stretch
4 Bent arm stretch
3 Arm press
48 Inner thigh lunge
55 Standing quads
58 Wall calf stretch
63 Wall Achilles stretch

## SWIMMING

Swimming is a sport that develops muscular endurance, strength and flexibility with a relatively low risk of injury. The physiques of elite swimmers show low body fat, good muscular development and muscular balance. Swimming also develops aerobic fitness.

The site of most injuries is the shoulder. The injury is often tendonitis. It is usually caused by either poor technique or a lack of balanced muscular development in the shoulder girdle. Shoulder injuries in swimmers can be avoided through appropriate training methods. It is important to supplement your training with 'land conditioning' – that is, weight training. Weight training can rectify the lack of muscular balance as well as adding strength and therefore speed.

**Injuries**     One method of avoiding injury is to avoid training for only one stroke. Different strokes develop different parts of the body and by training a variety of strokes you can achieve a balance of muscular development. For example, the back stroke develops flexibility in the shoulders. After a training session on one stroke, it is advisable to finish by swimming a few lengths of backstroke that will loosen the shoulders.

Breaststroke develops the upper arms, chest, thighs and hips. Butterfly develops the whole upper body and freestyle particularly develops the chest.

Swimming is an excellent substitute activity for sports people who are injured and cannot do any weight-bearing activity. It can help maintain endurance, strength and flexibility whilst athletes are unable to pursue normal training. Physiotherapists can prescribe swimming training schedules to assist injured athletes maintain muscle tone. More details of pool training recommendations for injured athletes are included in Part 2, 'Understanding Injuries'.

**Warm-up**     A swimmer's competition warm-up should include active static stretching following the sequence of stretches below, followed by mobilizing exercises for the shoulders within the ROM previously achieved (see pages 59–62).

- Swim 1500 metres of the pool slowly.
- Swim a few lengths at pace concentrating on technique.
- Swim two or three shorter, faster 25 or 50 metre repetitions.
- Maintain ROM until the competition starts by gentle mobilizing exercises.

A warm-up for training will include static stretching and mobilizing followed by a 1500-metre swim.

### *Swimming flexibility schedule*

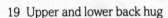

19  Upper and lower back hug
25  Sitting spinal twist
40  Sitting one-legged ham stretch
38  Sitting spinal hip rotation
49  Sitting inner thigh stretch
20  Shoulder stretch
 8  Overhead stretch
27  Behind back chest stretch
 9  Triceps stretch
11  Lats stretch
26  One-armed side stretch
 4  Bent arm stretch
55  Standing quads
58  Wall calf stretch
63  Wall Achilles stretch

## TENNIS

Playing tennis involves using all the main major muscle groups. It is a game that requires speed and strength. Top-class matches can last over two hours and players therefore also need substantial aerobic fitness.

Legs, arms and back play important roles in most tennis shots. Tennis also involves a lot of rotation, twisting and stretching movements. These

movements tend to lead to injuries in the shoulder, lower back and knee due to muscular imbalance and weak muscles. Flexibility is essential for tennis players of all standards to prepare for the dynamic nature of the game and to counteract the one-sided development that is an inevitable consequence of playing.

***Injuries*** The main injury associated with this sport is the infamous 'tennis elbow'. Tennis elbow is a term that covers many conditions. It refers to pain on the outside of the elbow. It is usually the result of inflammation that may have any number of causes. The main causes are playing with a racquet that is too heavy, poor technique, incorrect grip size, and muscular imbalance around the shoulders.

Other causes of injury include lack of physical condition and inadequate warm-up. The nature of the game, with its sudden changes of speed and direction, results in problems for the unprepared player.

Recreational tennis players must include a thorough warm-up before playing if they are to avoid serious injury. Elite players must train for speed, endurance and agility if they want to win matches at the highest level. Both groups should include flexibility exercises in their schedule whenever they play or train.

It is important to consider the surfaces on which you play. Grass or clay is usually better than the harder artificial courts. Ensure that your shoes are cushioned and designed for lateral movements. Running shoes are not suitable for tennis, despite being well cushioned, as they do not offer any lateral support. If you play on a once-a-week basis you are vulnerable to injury. One game a week puts you at risk of injury. Try to include some fitness training on a regular basis.

The main problem for elite players is that they tend to develop only one side of the body. Consequently they must do supplementary weight training and flexibility to provide balance.

**Warm-up**
- Jog around the court eight times.
- Mobilize the shoulders and back (see pages 55–64).
- Complete the flexibility schedule below.
- Rehearse your full range of shots with a partner.
- Practise full effort shots, particularly serves.

***Tennis flexibility schedule***

19  Upper and lower back hug
22  Lying back curl
33  Knee hug
42  Supine one-legged ham stretch
35  Crossed-leg gluteals
49  Sitting inner thigh stretch
52  Sitting straddle
38  Sitting spinal hip rotation
20  Shoulder stretch
 8  Overhead stretch
27  Behind back chest stretch
26  One-armed side stretch
 9  Triceps stretch
11  Lats stretch
 4  Bent arm stretch
 3  Arm press

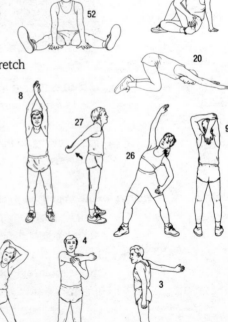

48 Inner thigh lunge
55 Standing quads
58 Wall calf stretch
63 Wall Achilles stretch

## VOLLEYBALL

Volleyball is a dynamic game. The physical demands of the game include aerobic endurance, strength, flexibility, speed and agility. In volleyball power needs to be explosive, so much attention is given to resistance and jump training (plyometrics). To perform a spike, it is necessary to be explosive in the jump, then hold position, then use an explosive arm movement to spike the ball. The torso needs to be firm to act as a stabilizer in the spike, though rotation must occur to spike the ball. Conditioning for volleyball includes development of aerobic and

anaerobic endurance, agility and flexibility. Speed is particularly important in a complete range of movement, from low positions (as in dives) to high (as in jumps). Rebound movements are common and demand high levels of elasticity in the muscles.

An amateur volleyball player trains on average 4 hours per week – 2 hours on 2 evenings. Some teams may train 6–8 hours per week, but this is the exception rather than the norm. Training tends to focus on technical aspects of volleyball, rather than fitness. This is because of the time constraints of hall bookings. If the team is training 4 hours a week, the coach understandably uses the time for technique and strategy. Consequently fitness is left to the discretion of individual players or a set programme is followed unsupervised. Flexibility may form a small part of the warm-up, but often lip service is paid to this important component of fitness.

Stretching exercises during the warm-up phase of training or a match will reduce the incidence of injury. Adequate flexibility for volleyball can also improve performance. For example, if the hitting arm is able to extend further back in the preparation phase for the spike, more force can be brought to bear on the ball. Strength is also vital in the spike. Both strength and flexibility can be developed to enhance performance. Resistance training is often performed in the off season to increase strength. Coaches should consider including a flexibility development programme to run alongside resistance training. PNF stretching would be particularly relevant for flexibility development.

### Injuries

According to statistics from Edinburgh University's Sports Injuries Centre, shoulder injuries are the most prevalent volleyball injury. This is followed by ankle injury, then back pain. Other less common injury sites include hips and groin, wrists and hands, thighs, feet, elbows and calf/Achilles, as well as shin splints.

Shoulder injuries and back pain are sometimes caused by an inadequate warm-up, or poor technique. For example, in the spike, if a player takes off on the wrong foot, rotation is awkward and the spike usually unsuccessful. Ankle injuries are mostly caused by the player landing on someone else's foot as they return from a jump. It is particularly common for inexperienced players to allow their feet to land on the opposition's side of the net. An opposing player then unfortunately lands on the inexperienced player's foot. Shin splints are quite common, usually caused by playing on hard surfaces.

***Warm-up***   Begin with a 5–10 minute easy jog to gradually raise the body temperature, blood flow, heart rate and metabolic processes. Next perform mobility exercises, beginning with the back exercises, then working from head to toe (see pages 55–64). Again begin with back exercises in the flexibility schedule below, then work from head to toe. Pay particular attention to shoulders and backs. After static stretching, rehearse volleyball movements before continuing with set practices.

At the end of training or a match, don't forget to cool down with light jogging and static stretching exercises.

### Volleyball flexibility schedule

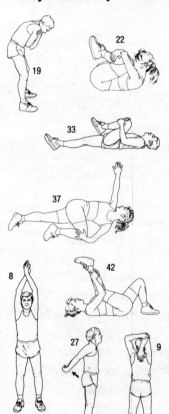

19  Upper and lower back hug
22  Lying back curl
33  Knee hug
37  Supine spinal rotation
42  Supine one-legged ham stretch
 8  Overhead stretch
27  Behind back chest stretch
 9  Triceps stretch
11  Lats stretch
26  One-armed side stretch
12  Wrist reach
15  Assisted wrist flexors
34  Kneeling hip stretch
38  Sitting spinal hip rotation
49  Sitting inner thigh stretch
52  Sitting straddle
48  Inner thigh lunge
55  Standing quads
58  Wall calf stretch
63  Wall Achilles stretch

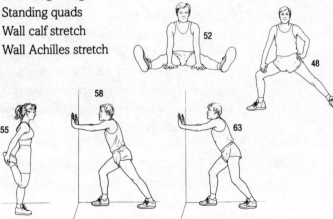

## WALKING/HILL WALKING

Walking and hill walking are very popular forms of recreation, ranging from a couple of hours to several days backpacking with full rucksacks. It is not necessary to be super fit to participate in hill walking, but a certain amount of physical fitness will aid maximum enjoyment. Participants should be prepared for the length of walk, with above-average cardio-respiratory fitness, muscular strength and endurance and flexibility.

During steep ascents calf muscles often tighten up and thigh and buttock muscles fatigue. Descending from a hill creates a greater impact on the body as each step creates a greater impact force. Individuals with a history of ankle and knee injury should take particular care whilst descending. Strengthening the leg muscles provides some protection against the risk of injury.

*Injuries*  The most common injuries in walking occur in the legs, mainly the knee but also calf, Achilles and ankle, as well as in the back. Less common injuries include hip, groin and foot injuries. Some of these injuries could be avoided by generally improving fitness before going walking, especially on a backpacking trip. A mobility warm-up, stretching all major leg muscles before embarking on a walk, is also advisable. When walking it is wise to stop and stretch out the muscles at the onset of muscle tightness. Common areas of tightness include the calf and thigh areas.

**Warm-up**  The majority of walkers never stop to consider a warm-up because walking is such an everyday activity. However, walking up and down a high or steep hill is a different matter and care should be taken to prepare the body for the activity ahead. A mobility warm up before setting out is ideal (see pages 55–64).

If a heavy rucksack is to be carried, special attention should be focused on warming up the back. Stretching leg muscles is particularly important (gastrocnemius, soleus, quadriceps and hamstrings). See the schedule below for suggested stretches. After the walk is over it is advisable to repeat the stretches again to reduce stiffness.

*Walking flexibility schedule*

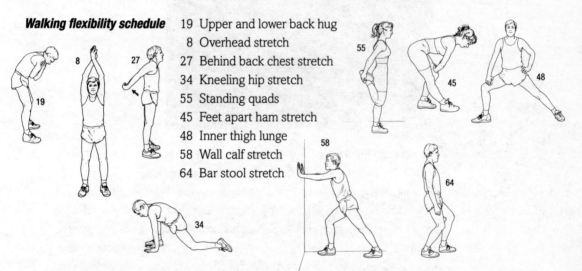

19  Upper and lower back hug
 8  Overhead stretch
27  Behind back chest stretch
34  Kneeling hip stretch
55  Standing quads
45  Feet apart ham stretch
48  Inner thigh lunge
58  Wall calf stretch
64  Bar stool stretch

# WEIGHT TRAINING

An increasing number of people are including weight training in their fitness programmes. Some use weights as a means of improving their performance in another sport, whilst others use weight training as an activity in its own right. They enjoy the health benefits that weight training brings. A smaller group participates in competitive weight lifting. There are two schools of competitive weight lifting: Olympic and Power. **Weight training** is the term given to the non-competitive sport. **Weight lifting** refers to the competitive sport.

Weight training will produce a variety of physical qualities. A schedule

of training can produce strength, muscular endurance or power. Power is the ability to move weight quickly. Muscular endurance is the ability to repeat a movement that requires strength many times. Weight training may develop firm muscle or large muscle. Different schedules produce different outcomes. You need to be clear as to the outcomes you want to achieve. If you are a beginner at weight training, it is vital to obtain expert advice to help you formulate these objectives, and how to achieve them, before embarking on a training programme.

Weight training involves the use of a wide variety of equipment. Machines, barbells and dumb-bells are required for serious weight trainers. Many weight trainers only use machines for their training. There is a range of reputable multi-gym machines that are safe and easy to use. If you are unable to obtain expert advice on weight training with barbells and dumb-bells, you can still do effective training by using multi-gym machines.

However, be careful when you progress to free weights (dumb-bells and barbells) from machines. You will not be able to lift the same weight as you did on the machines. A bench press exercise with a barbell and discs that total 40 kilograms (88 pounds) is much more difficult than a machine bench press with 40 kilograms. The machines are very effective in supporting the weight for the user and not requiring a great effort from fixator (supporting) muscles. Using machines does not require a great deal of technique. Training with free weights requires significant work from supporting muscles, and skill in lifting. It is therefore more demanding.

**Injuries** Weight training produces very few injuries, providing you have a good technique and do not lift heavy weights. Your technique is most likely to break down when you lift heavy weights. Beginners must spend several training sessions in learning lifting techniques whilst using light weights. The weight should be light enough to lift twenty consecutive times without alteration in technique.

When you have achieved a sound technique, you may want to try to lift heavy weights. Lifting heavy weights will develop strength and muscle size. A heavy weight is usually defined as one that you can lift no more than eight times. Injuries sometimes occur at this stage simply due to accidents. You may overestimate your strength and fail to complete a lift. Remember to train with a partner who will act as a 'spotter' – that is, someone who will take the weights from you if you cannot complete a lift. It is also advisable to use a weight training belt to give support to your lower back.

While injuries in weight training are few, the main sites of injury are wrists, knees and shoulders. The primary reason for injury, apart from accidents and poor technique, is muscular imbalance.

**Warm-up** The warm-up for a weight training session starts with 3 to 4 minutes of slow jogging or alternative aerobic activity, such as the rowing machine or stationary bike. Then you need to follow the flexibility prescription below. Finally, start your weight training with one set of twenty repetitions of each exercise in your training schedule. Lift very light weights (at about 50 per cent of your maximum capacity) whilst rehearsing technique. Once you start the lifting session, take the opportunity between sets to loosen the muscles with active static stretching.

Weight lifters will follow a similar warm-up. They should add to the above schedule a thorough psychological preparation. Without completely focusing on the task, technique will disappear and damage can be done to the body.

**Weight training flexibility schedule**
19 Upper and lower back hug
25 Sitting spinal twist
49 Sitting inner thigh stretch
*Continues over*

52 Sitting straddle
40 Sitting one-legged ham stretch
8 Overhead stretch
27 Behind back chest stretch
26 One-armed side stretch
4 Bent arm stretch
9 Triceps stretch
11 Lats stretch
55 Standing quads
58 Wall calf stretch
63 Wall Achilles stretch

# Glossary

**Abduction** movement of a limb away from the mid-line of the body, as in raising the arm horizontally.

**Actin** one of the proteins found in muscle that is partly responsible for contraction.

**Active stretching** elongation of a muscle through an individual's own efforts. There is no assistance from an external agency. *See also* passive stretching.

**Adduction** movement of a limb towards the mid-line of the body, as in lowering a raised arm from the horizontal position.

**Aerobic** a biochemical pathway that requires oxygen to produce energy. It is associated with endurance events.

**Agonist** a muscle that is contracting.

**Anaerobic** a biochemical pathway that produces energy without the presence of oxygen. It is associated with short bursts of dynamic activity, as in sprinting.

**Antagonist** a muscle that relaxes and lengthens when the opposite muscle, the agonist, is contracting.

**Ballistic stretching** dynamic stretching. It is characterized by small, fast bouncing movements on the muscle at the end of its range.

**Circuit training** a form of fitness training. It normally involves a series of strength exercises arranged to develop strength and muscular endurance.

**Concentric contraction** the process of developing tension within a muscle while it shortens.

**Dynamic flexibility** involves motion of a joint or joints through a wide range at fast speeds.

**Eccentric contraction** the process of developing tension within a muscle while it is lengthening.

**Extension** a movement at a joint that increases the angle between two bones.

**Flexibility** the ability to move muscles and joints through their full range of motion. Flexibility is developed by stretching.

**Flexion** a movement at a joint that decreases the angle between two bones.

**Insertion** the end of a muscle that moves most when the muscle contracts.

**Isometric contraction** the process by which a change in tension occurs in a muscle, but the length of the muscle does not change. An example is when one tries to lift a piano with one hand.

**Isotonic contraction** a change in tension that occurs in a muscle and is accompanied by a change in the length of the muscle. An example is the biceps muscle of the arm when you flex and extend the elbow while holding a weight in your hand.

**Myosin** one of the proteins found in muscle that is partly responsible for contraction.

**Mobilizing exercise** a type of exercise designed to loosen joints.

**Origin** the end of a muscle that moves least when the muscle contracts.

**Passive stretching** elongating a muscle by using an external agent, such as a partner.

**Plyometrics** a form of athletic training designed to improve power. It involves an eccentric contraction of a muscle quickly followed by a concentric contraction. Usually takes the form of jumping, hopping and bounding.

**PNF stretching** proprioceptive neuromuscular facilitation. An effective way to lengthen muscle, involving a variety of techniques including hold–relax, contract–relax and contract–relax–agonist–contract. All these methods require a contraction and relaxation of the target muscle.

**Prone** lying on your stomach.

**ROM** range of motion; the flexibility in a joint or group of joints.

**Static stretching** moving a muscle to an extended position and holding the position for a period of time.

**Supine** lying on your back.

# Further Reading

Alter, M. J., *Science of Stretching*, Human Kinetics Books, 1988.

Borms, J. et al, 'Optimal Duration of Static Stretching Exercises for Improvement of Coxo-femoral Flexibility', *Journal of Sports Sciences*, 1987, 5, 39–47.

Etnyre, B. R. and Lee, E. J., 'Comments on Proprioceptive Neuromuscular Facilitation Stretching Techniques', *Research Quarterly for Exercise and Sport*, 1987, Vol. 58, No. 2, pp. 184–88.

Hardy, L., 'Improving Active Range of Hip Flexion', *Research Quarterly for Exercise and Sport*, 1985, Vol. 56, No. 2, pp. 111–14.

Hardy, L. and Jones, D., 'Dynamic Flexibility and Proprioceptive Neuromuscular Facilitation', *Research Quarterly for Exercise and Sport*, 1986, Vol. 57, pp. 105–53.

Jackson, A. W. and Baker, A. A., 'The Relationship of the Sit and Reach Test to Criterion Measures of Hamstring and Back Flexibility in Young Females', *Research Quarterly for Exercise and Sport*, 1986, Vol. 57, pp. 183–86.

McAtee, R. E., *Facilitated Stretching*, Human Kinetics Publishers, 1993.

Marieb, E. N., *Human Anatomy and Physiology*, The Benjamin/Cummings Publishing Company, Inc., 1989.

Sady, S. P. et al, 'Flexibility Training: Ballistic, Static or Proprioceptive Neuromuscular Facilitation?', *Arch Phys Med Rehabil*, June 1982, Vol. 63.

Snell, R. S., *Clinical Anatomy for Medical Students*, Little Brown, 1986.

Taylor, D. C., et al, 'Viscoelastic Properties of Muscle-tendon Units', *American Journal of Sports Medicine*, 1990, Vol. 18, No. 3.

Wilkinson, A., 'Stretching the Truth: A Review of the Literature on Muscle Stretching', *Australian Physiotherapy*, 1992, Vol. 38, No. 4.

Williford, H. N. and Smith, J. F., 'A Comparison of Proprioceptive Neuromuscular Facilitation and Static Stretching Techniques', *Amer. Corr. Ther. J.* 1985, Vol. 39, No. 2.

Wirhed, R., *Athletic Ability and the Anatomy of Motion*, Wolfe Medical Publications Ltd., 1987.

# Appendix

The University of Edinburgh established a Sports Injury Clinic in 1988. Since 1990, the clinic staff have collected data on a variety of aspects of injuries. Of particular interest is the information on which sports produce the most injuries and the location of the injuries.

**Number of Injuries by Sport 1990–1991**

The sports that appear to be associated with most injuries are football, running, rugby, squash and athletics. However, it is clear that the sports that produce the most injuries are those for which the university provides facilities, coaching and competition. When one takes into account the size of the competition and training programme, the number of participants in each sport, and the proximity of the Sports Injury Clinic to particular facilities, it is clear that these are not necessarily the sports that produce the most 'risks'.

It is interesting to note which sports have large numbers of participants and an apparent low rate of injury. The University has an extensive aerobics programme. Like most sports centres it caters for a variety of classes including step, low impact and 'sweat sessions'. It also has a wide range of weight training equipment, including free weights. Classes are run in these activities. Despite the large number of participants in these activities, the number of injuries is low. Of particular interest is the fact that a very popular circuit training programme has produced very few injuries.

A common factor in these 'low risk' sports is that they are non-contact. They do not involve an opponent, thereby eliminating the risk of injury through collisions, accidental or otherwise. Secondly, at the University of Edinburgh, aerobics, weight training and circuit training have a comprehensive introductory programme. The courses are taught by qualified physical education teachers. A major principle in the development of these courses is the prevention of injury. Emphasis is placed on adequate warm-up, progressive and gradual increase in training loads, and on-going flexibility training. It is probable that the appropriate education of participants contributes to the low rate of injury.

The following charts indicate, for any particular sport, the sites of the body that are most frequently injured. Certain sports tend to place particular parts of the body at disproportionate risk. Football produces a large number of ankle and knee injuries. These two sites account for approximately 50 per cent of all football injuries. Over 50 per cent of skiing injuries afflict the knee.

In contrast, squash, tennis, badminton and rugby have a more varied pattern of injury. These statistics, whilst not surprising, do help to focus attention on the requirement for specific conditioning in sport. Coaches who are aware of the information contained in these charts can prepare training schedules that will develop the physical qualities needed to reduce the risk of injury.

**Number of Injuries by Sport 1990–1991**

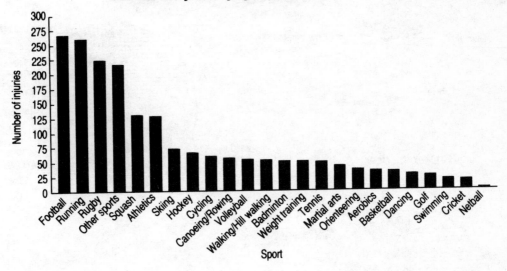

**Aerobics injuries**

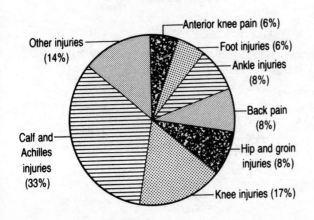

**Athletics injuries**

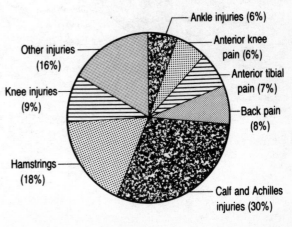

## Badminton injuries

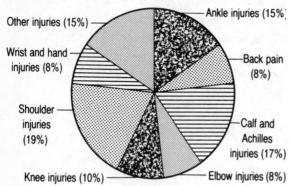

Other injuries (15%)
Ankle injuries (15%)
Wrist and hand injuries (8%)
Back pain (8%)
Shoulder injuries (19%)
Calf and Achilles injuries (17%)
Knee injuries (10%)
Elbow injuries (8%)

## Basketball injuries

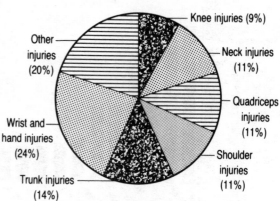

Knee injuries (9%)
Neck injuries (11%)
Quadriceps injuries (11%)
Shoulder injuries (11%)
Other injuries (20%)
Wrist and hand injuries (24%)
Trunk injuries (14%)

## Cricket injuries

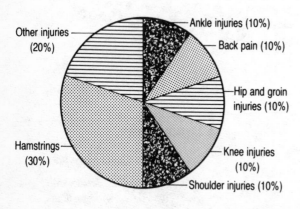

Ankle injuries (10%)
Back pain (10%)
Hip and groin injuries (10%)
Knee injuries (10%)
Shoulder injuries (10%)
Other injuries (20%)
Hamstrings (30%)

## Cycling injuries

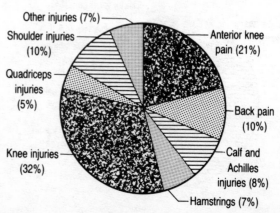

Other injuries (7%)
Anterior knee pain (21%)
Shoulder injuries (10%)
Quadriceps injuries (5%)
Back pain (10%)
Knee injuries (32%)
Calf and Achilles injuries (8%)
Hamstrings (7%)

## Dance injuries

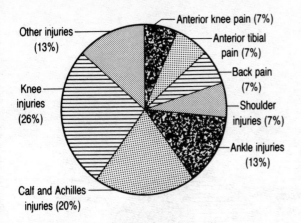

Anterior knee pain (7%)
Anterior tibial pain (7%)
Back pain (7%)
Shoulder injuries (7%)
Ankle injuries (13%)
Calf and Achilles injuries (20%)
Knee injuries (26%)
Other injuries (13%)

## Football injuries

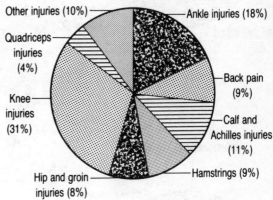

Other injuries (10%)
Quadriceps injuries (4%)
Knee injuries (31%)
Hip and groin injuries (8%)
Ankle injuries (18%)
Back pain (9%)
Calf and Achilles injuries (11%)
Hamstrings (9%)

## Golf injuries

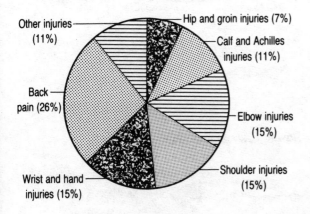

Other injuries (11%)
Back pain (26%)
Wrist and hand injuries (15%)
Hip and groin injuries (7%)
Calf and Achilles injuries (11%)
Elbow injuries (15%)
Shoulder injuries (15%)

## Hockey injuries

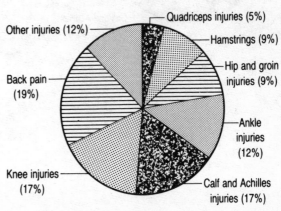

Other injuries (12%)
Back pain (19%)
Knee injuries (17%)
Quadriceps injuries (5%)
Hamstrings (9%)
Hip and groin injuries (9%)
Ankle injuries (12%)
Calf and Achilles injuries (17%)

## Martial arts injuries

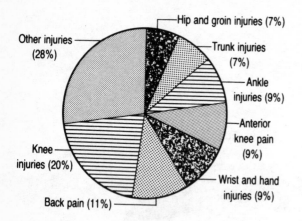

Hip and groin injuries (7%)
Trunk injuries (7%)
Ankle injuries (9%)
Anterior knee pain (9%)
Wrist and hand injuries (9%)
Back pain (11%)
Knee injuries (20%)
Other injuries (28%)

## Netball injuries

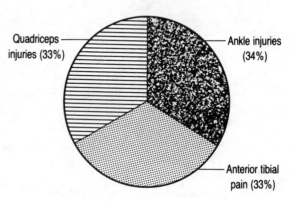

Quadriceps injuries (33%)
Ankle injuries (34%)
Anterior tibial pain (33%)

## Orienteering injuries

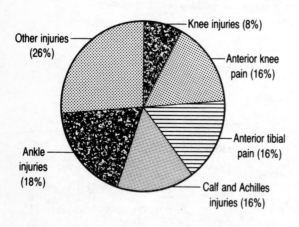

Knee injuries (8%)
Anterior knee pain (16%)
Anterior tibial pain (16%)
Calf and Achilles injuries (16%)
Ankle injuries (18%)
Other injuries (26%)

## Rowing/Canoeing/Kayaking injuries

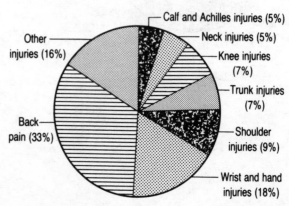

Calf and Achilles injuries (5%)
Neck injuries (5%)
Knee injuries (7%)
Trunk injuries (7%)
Shoulder injuries (9%)
Wrist and hand injuries (18%)
Back pain (33%)
Other injuries (16%)

## Rugby injuries

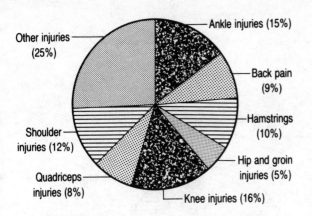

Other injuries (25%)
Ankle injuries (15%)
Back pain (9%)
Hamstrings (10%)
Shoulder injuries (12%)
Hip and groin injuries (5%)
Quadriceps injuries (8%)
Knee injuries (16%)

## Running injuries

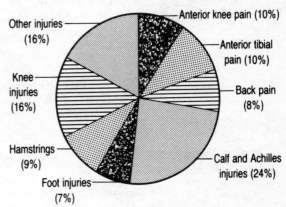

Other injuries (16%)
Anterior knee pain (10%)
Anterior tibial pain (10%)
Knee injuries (16%)
Back pain (8%)
Hamstrings (9%)
Foot injuries (7%)
Calf and Achilles injuries (24%)

## Skiing injuries

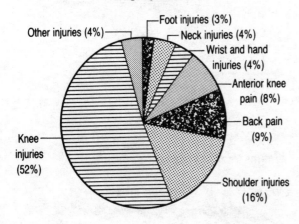

Other injuries (4%)
Foot injuries (3%)
Neck injuries (4%)
Wrist and hand injuries (4%)
Anterior knee pain (8%)
Back pain (9%)
Knee injuries (52%)
Shoulder injuries (16%)

## Squash injuries

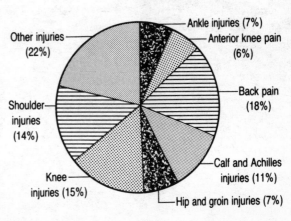

Other injuries (22%)
Ankle injuries (7%)
Anterior knee pain (6%)
Back pain (18%)
Shoulder injuries (14%)
Calf and Achilles injuries (11%)
Knee injuries (15%)
Hip and groin injuries (7%)

## Swimming injuries

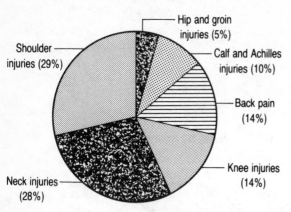

- Hip and groin injuries (5%)
- Shoulder injuries (29%)
- Calf and Achilles injuries (10%)
- Back pain (14%)
- Knee injuries (14%)
- Neck injuries (28%)

## Tennis injuries

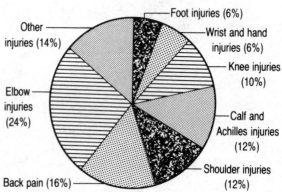

- Foot injuries (6%)
- Other injuries (14%)
- Wrist and hand injuries (6%)
- Knee injuries (10%)
- Elbow injuries (24%)
- Calf and Achilles injuries (12%)
- Shoulder injuries (12%)
- Back pain (16%)

## Walking (Hill walking) injuries

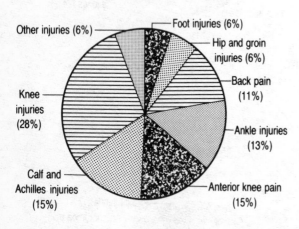

- Other injuries (6%)
- Foot injuries (6%)
- Hip and groin injuries (6%)
- Back pain (11%)
- Knee injuries (28%)
- Ankle injuries (13%)
- Calf and Achilles injuries (15%)
- Anterior knee pain (15%)

## Weight training injuries

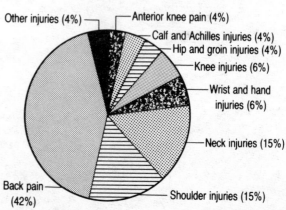

- Other injuries (4%)
- Anterior knee pain (4%)
- Calf and Achilles injuries (4%)
- Hip and groin injuries (4%)
- Knee injuries (6%)
- Wrist and hand injuries (6%)
- Neck injuries (15%)
- Back pain (42%)
- Shoulder injuries (15%)

# Index